D1124163

THE MAKING OF THE ENGLISH LANDSCAPE

★

LANCASHIRE

THE MAKING OF THE ENGLISH LANDSCAPE

EDITED BY W. G. HOSKINS

---

1. THE MAKING OF THE ENGLISH LANDSCAPE	W. G. HOSKINS
2. CORNWALL	W. G. V. BALCHIN
3. LANCASHIRE	ROY MILLWARD
4. GLOUCESTERSHIRE	H. P. R. FINBERG

IN PREPARATION

5. LEICESTERSHIRE AND RUTLAND	W. G. HOSKINS

LANCASHIRE

AN ILLUSTRATED ESSAY ON THE HISTORY OF THE LANDSCAPE

by

ROY MILLWARD

Lecturer in Historical Geography at University College, Leicester

LONDON
HODDER AND STOUGHTON
1955

TO
MY PARENTS

First Printed 1955

Printed in Great Britain for Hodder and Stoughton, Ltd.
by Billing and Sons Ltd., Guildford and London

Contents

ACKNOWLEDGMENTS

THE author wishes to acknowledge photographs from the following sources: Dr. E. M. Adcock (Plates 4 and 25); Aerofilms Ltd. (Plates 19 and 29); British Railways (Plates 43, 44, and 45); British Travel and Holidays Association (Plate 13); J. Hardman (Plates 2, 8, and 12); H. S. Hodgson (Plates 33 and 39); R. Kirkham (Plate 46); Kemsley Newspapers Ltd., Manchester (Plate 16); P. Marsden (Plate 38); W. Rhodes Marriott (Plates 20 and 37); *Oldham Chronicle* (Plate 3); *Preston Guardian* (Plate 11); *Southport Visiter* (Plate 36); *The Times* (Plate 47).

Plates 21, 22, 26, and 27 are from W. H. Pyne's *Lancashire Illustrated* (1831).

The remainder of the photographs were specially taken by the author (Plates 1, 5, 6, 7, 9, 10, 14, 15, 17, 18, 23, 24, 28, 30, 31, 32, 34, 35, 40, 41, 42, 48, 49, and 50).

I am particularly indebted to T. Garfield of the Department of Geography, University College, Leicester, who prepared the maps for publication.

I would like to thank all those who have helped me in gathering material for this book and especially R. Sharpe-France, Lancashire County Archivist, who read through the manuscript and offered valuable criticism; F. Barnes (Librarian of Barrow-in-Furness); G. M. Bland (Librarian of the Lancaster City Library); G. A. Carter (Librarian of Warrington); H. C. Caistor (Librarian of St. Helens); G. F. Foster (Librarian of Ashton-under-Lyne); W. B. Leeming (Librarian of Fleetwood); Miss T. Simpson (Director of the Central Public Library at Oldham) who gave access to local collections; and, not least, Professor Cordingley of the School of Architecture, Manchester University, who allowed me to use a vast store of unpublished research on domestic architecture and building materials in Lancashire. If any errors remain after all this help, the fault is mine alone.

ROY MILLWARD.

Leicester.

List of Plates

List of Maps

A map of the county showing all places mentioned in the text will be found on pp. 56-57.

Editor's Introduction

DESPITE the multitude of books about English landscape and scenery, and the flood of topographical books in general, there is not one book which deals with the historical evolution of the landscape as we know it. At the most we may be told that the English landscape is the man-made creation of the seventeenth and eighteenth centuries, which is not even a quarter-truth, for it refers only to country houses and their parks and to the parliamentary enclosures that gave us a good deal of our modern pattern of fields, hedges, and by-roads. It ignores the fact that more than a half of England never underwent this kind of enclosure, but evolved in an entirely different way, and that in some regions the landscape had been virtually completed by the eve of the Black Death. No book exists to describe the manner in which the various landscapes of this country came to assume the shape and appearance they now have, why the hedgebanks and lanes of Devon should be so totally different from those of the Midlands, why there are so many ruined churches in Norfolk or so many lost villages in Lincolnshire, or what history lies behind the winding ditches of the Somerset marshlands, the remote granite farmsteads of Cornwall, and the lonely pastures of upland Northamptonshire.

There are, indeed, some good books on the geology that lies behind the English landscape, and these represent perhaps the best kind of writing on the subject we have yet had, for they deal with facts and are not given to the sentimental and formless slush which afflicts so many books concerned only with superficial appearances. But the geologist, good though he may be, is concerned with only one aspect of the subject, and beyond a certain point he is obliged to leave the historian and geographer to continue and complete it. He explains to us the bones of the landscape, the fundamental structure that gives form and colour to the scene and produces a certain kind of topography and natural vegetation. But the flesh that covers the bones, and the details of the features, are the concern of the historical geographer, whose task it is to show how man has clothed the geological skeleton during the comparatively recent past—mostly within the last fifteen centuries, though in some regions much longer than this. These books on *The Making of the English Landscape* set out to do this, county by county and region by region.

The authors of these books are concerned with the ways in which men have cleared the natural woodlands, reclaimed marshland, fen, and moor, created fields out of a wilderness, made lanes, roads, and footpaths, laid out towns, built villages, hamlets, farmhouses and cottages, created country houses and their parks, dug mines and made canals and railways, in short with everything that has altered the natural landscape. One cannot understand the English landscape and enjoy it to the full, apprehend all its wonderful variety from region to region (often within the space of a few miles), without going back to the history that lies behind it. A commonplace ditch may be the thousand-year-old boundary of a royal manor; a certain hedgebank may be even more ancient, the boundary of a Celtic estate; a certain deep and winding lane may be the work of twelfth-century peasants, some of whose names may be made known to us if we search diligently enough. To discover these things we have to go to the documents that are the historian's raw material, and find out what happened to produce these results and when, and precisely how they came about. But it is not only the documents that are the historian's guide. One cannot write books like these by reading someone else's books, or even by studying records in a muniment room. The English landscape itself, to those who know how to read it aright, is the richest historical record we possess. There are discoveries to be made in it for which no written documents exist, or have ever existed. To write the history of the English landscape requires a combination of documentary research and of fieldwork, of laborious scrambling on foot wherever the trail may lead. The result is a new kind of history which it is hoped will appeal to all those who like to travel intelligently, to get away from the guide-book show-pieces now and then, and to know the reasons behind what they are looking at. There is no part of England, however unpromising it may appear at first sight, that is not full of questions for those who have a sense of the past. So much of England is still unknown and unexplored. Fuller enjoined us nearly three centuries ago

> Know most of the rooms of thy native country before thou goest over the threshold thereof. Especially seeing England presents thee with so many observables.

These books on *The Making of the English Landscape* are concerned with the observables of England, and the secret history that lies behind them.

W. G. HOSKINS.

OXFORD,
December, 1953.

I

The Lancashire Scene

FROM its frontier with Cheshire along the Mersey to the bare sands and salt marshes of the Duddon, the Lancashire plain is framed to the north and east by mountains. Nowhere is this plain of any great extent; from nearly every hill-top the western horizon is closed by the Irish Sea. If you climb a Lancashire hill, decorated by one of the many monumental towers commemorating some unforgettable event in national history or some dim forgotten part of the local story, a wide view opens up which often includes most of the county. Two elements are always present: the drab moorlands, seamed with stone walls, fade away, one billowy horizon behind another, eastward into Yorkshire; and the grey-green plain spreads at one's feet, interrupted by the dark smudges of towns and the thin pencils of factory chimneys, streaming out their smoke screens on the westerly winds.

The Pennines, composed of a succession of dreary, treeless plateaus, make up the eastern wall of Lancashire. The wetter parts are covered with a deep blanket of peat, and the rocks beneath are hard sandstones of the Millstone Grit and the Coal Measures. When the bare rock is exposed in the beds of streams, it forms large angular slabs varying in colour according to the composition of the sandstone, from a silvery grey through a subtle range of purples to a rich rust.

An important group of moorlands, collectively known as Rossendale Forest, thrusts far westward from the Pennines into the Lancashire plain, forming one of the most individual regions in the county. The scenery of plateau-like hills and deep valleys is carved out of a thick series of sandstones, shales, and valuable seams of coal. Dark bluffs of sandstone form part of the horizon in almost every Rossendale valley. Turned to more useful purposes by the hand of man these hard freestones can be seen in every part of this upland in the miles of dry stone walls, built in the last century at a few pence per yard to fence in the sullen earth of mountain farms. The industrial towns, such as Haslingden, Bacup, and Crawshaw Booth, have been built almost entirely of this sombre grey stone (Plate 1). The quarries from which the rock was hewn in enormous quantities since the middle of the eighteenth century are now largely abandoned. Bright mosses colonize the bare rock faces from which the stone was cut, and heather slowly finds a foothold in the masses of angular waste that were tipped down the hillsides.

Climate adds its tones to the harsh scenery of Rossendale, of which perhaps the most enduring feature is a grey lid of clouds. The sun shines here far less often than in the plain, and the annual rainfall is several inches higher. The sober facts of climatology express themselves more vividly in the common experience of leaving Haslingden on a morning of endless, quickly moving banks of cloud and drenching showers of cold rain and spending the day at Blackpool in sunshine whose brilliance can match that of the Mediterranean. The hard climate of Rossendale combined with the poor soils has left a perpetual impression on the farming of the district. For centuries these uplands have had a tradition of pastoralism. In the Middle Ages cattle grazed the thinly wooded hillsides above the "booths," names that have come down from the medieval farms to the industrial hamlets of today. Even today, when a second world war has greatly

PLATE 1

Facit: short stone-built terraces in a narrow Rossendale valley with abandoned quarries on the hillside. Facit was originally a thirteenth-century settlement: the name means "the bright, flowery slope."

extended the acres of arable land in England, there is scarcely a ploughed field in the whole region. The land is too ungrateful.

The events of history too have left their mark on this district, moulding the detail of the landscape to its present shape. The remains of a Roman road follow the height of the land from Bury to beyond Darwen, in part forming the boundaries of parishes that were created before the Norman Conquest. The place-names ending in "booth" recall the medieval cattle-farmers who first colonized and left a permanent impression on this wilderness. "Booth" comes from the old Scandinavian word for "cow house, herdsman's hut." A later stream of settlers flowed into this moorland in the sixteenth and seventeenth centuries, founding small farms and manufacturing cloth. Later, the Industrial Revolution filled the valleys with grim stone mills and long rows of cottages. This landscape of lonely hill farms and grey towns, constricted in the folds of the moors, has been formed in the image of men's ideas and under the pressure of social and economic movements as much as by the blind processes of nature.

North of the Ribble the hills are much more varied in their rocks and scenery. Bowland Forest is a tangle of deep valleys and bare moors projecting westward from the main body of the Pennines into the plain of the Fylde. Its rocks—shales and sandstones of Millstone Grit age—contain no valuable coal seams, a fact that has profoundly influenced the history and the landscape of the region. Unlike Rossendale, it has escaped the scars of the Industrial Revolution. It is a district of upland sheep farms; and on the margins, where communication is easier, quarrying has become an important occupation. The elegant grey houses of Lancaster were built from stone quarried in these hills. Longridge, on the southern edge of Bowland Forest, grew into a small town because its quarries provided a good building stone that was in demand all over Lancashire in the nineteenth century. Many of Preston's public buildings are of this sandstone, and it was used by Paley and Austen, the Lancaster architects, when they rebuilt the parish church at Bolton between 1867 and 1871.

Northwards again, beyond the valley of the Lune, the scene is still more varied. Around Carnforth the pale pastures and bare white scars tell us that the underlying rock is the Carboniferous Limestone. Besides forming the foundations of the landscape at the head of Morecambe Bay—perhaps the most attractive scenery in the county—the cool grey tones of this local rock have entered into the man-made details of the countryside. Silver-grey walls, lighter than the surrounding fields, wriggle across the treeless hillsides. Farms and barns, where they have not been covered with the favoured coat of roughcast, harmonize with these angular limestone hills. There is a cool and luminous quality in this landscape, especially perhaps when the sea mists creep in across the treacherous sands and salt-marshes of Morecambe Bay.

The rocks of High Furness, across Morecambe Bay, are the oldest in Lancashire. They belong to the volcanic rocks that form the bulk of the Lake District (Plate 2). The low hills of the Furness Fells, which scarcely rise above a thousand feet, generally coincide with flags, grits and leaden-coloured mudstones of Silurian age, rocks which in the past have been abundantly worked for building stone and roofing slates.

Above Coniston the Borrowdale Volcanics form the mountain group of Wetherlam and the Old Man. They consist of ashes and lavas that were poured on to the floor of a sea in a remote geological past. The volcanic ashes have since been changed into hard and valuable slates under the immense compressive forces of a mountain-building movement. On these few acres of true mountain summit one reaches the only natural landscape in the county apart from the coastal strips of empty salt-marsh and mudflats swept by the changing tides. The tumbled masses of rounded boulders that bury the mountain tops, sparsely colonized by mosses and bright yellow lichens, take us into a region whose climate and vegetation can only be matched in the sub-Arctic tundras.

If one stands on the summit of the Coniston Fells, with Goat Water far below holding out a mirror to the changing sky, it is hard to believe that we are still in Lancashire. It was the distribution of land to the followers of William the Conqueror that linked this piece of the Lake District with the county that contains

PLATE 2

A natural landscape in the Duddon valley.

Wigan and Widnes. Yet, since the Romantic Movement discovered the qualities of the British mountains and Ruskin settled on the shores of Coniston Water, the guide books to Lancashire have not let their readers forget this enclave of another world in Furness. Many, indeed, write only of the beauties of the north of the county to the exclusion of the rest. Even today, there is a tendency to believe that the rich history of Lancashire, so much of it belonging to the nineteenth century and as yet barely explored, can be dismissed with the familiar story of the Pendle witches and a collection of photographs of the "beauty spots" in Furness and Cartmel.

The Lancashire hills form the backcloth to the plain, that setting for all the big industrial towns and the place where most of the county's wealth has been made and the richest dramas of its history enacted. The south-eastern part of the plain, hemmed in by a semicircle of bare moors from Bolton to Ashton-under-Lyne, turns towards Manchester as its capital city. The relationship between the textile towns—Bolton, Bury, Rochdale, Oldham—and the commercial centre of the cotton industry was first established in the seventeenth century when the merchants of Manchester began to organize the manufacture of wool and linen in the surrounding countryside. The immense attractive power of the capital city is seen today in the labyrinth of railways that connect Manchester with its neighbouring towns and the web of trunk roads that converge on the city. The derelict canals, threading the despoiled valleys that lead down from the rim of hills, bear witness too to the same magnetic force at work in the closing years of the eighteenth century.

Most of the rocks that break the surface in this south-eastern plain belong to the Lower and Middle Coal Measures. A walk along any of the streams emptying into the Irwell provides a fair sample of the scenery of this region. The landforms are soft and open where a valley crosses the blue-grey shales, but the hard rust-red sandstones, occurring at various levels in the thick series of shales and coal seams, form miniature gorges, dense with trees and often harbouring the sites of ruined mills.

The presence of a number of good coal seams at the surface led this district to become one of the first centres of the Industrial Revolution. Names like the Worsley Four Foot, the Parker Mine, and the Bradford Four Foot Coal, recall the famous seams that have given up their wealth to cover this countryside with drab industrial hamlets and mill-towns. Most of the shallow surface seams are now exhausted. Abandoned buildings and barren slag heaps, now being levelled for playing fields and council houses, form part of the landscape in almost every industrial town. Milnrow, a grey stone town close to Rochdale, used to have two coal mines—the Jubilee and Butterworth Hall. Both are now closed and the flooded workings of Butterworth Hall were bought by Oldham Corporation in 1930 to be used as a reservoir. All over this region small mines stand derelict; and its other staple industry, cotton-spinning, has been severely diminished by the years of depression before 1939. Many of the huge spinning mills—five stories of glass and terra-cotta—have been demolished; only their chimney stacks stand as symbols of their former pride. In many other mills floors have been sub-let to smaller industries—they manufacture wallpaper, put paint and varnish into tins or beer in bottles, or assemble radios.

The Manchester plain is probably the drabbest scene in the county. The pallid fields wear eternally a veneer of industrial grime, while the Irwell and its tributaries are little more than open drains for the waste of all the mills upon their banks. The very air is always grey with the smoke of the huge towns that fill the plain. Only on the rare days when a clear stream of polar air sweeps across

Lancashire from the north-west, rolling back the canopy of smoke, can one look across the plain to take in at one glance the whole rampart of encircling moors. Then from Holcombe Hill, with its Peel monument built in 1852 to commemorate the repeal of the Corn Laws, the whole of this ganglion of the Industrial Revolution lies spread like a map at one's feet—the towns forming huge dark smudges on a dull green quilt (Plate 3).

The rest of the plain, between the Mersey and the Ribble, contains two distinct physical regions with histories of their own. The higher part, to the east, lies on the Coal Measures; and today the deep mines around Leigh and Wigan form one of the most productive parts of the Lancashire coalfield. Heavy industry—cotton-spinning, mining, and engineering—has left a deep mark on the landscape of this belt. Mining started in this area at least seven centuries ago. There is clear

PLATE 3

Royton: a cotton town and a creation of the Industrial Revolution.

proof of it in Leland's *Itinerary*, written about 1540. He noted the "canale and cole pittes in divers parts of Darbyshire" (*i.e.*, the West Derby Hundred of Lancashire) and a "great mine of canale at Haigh" near Wigan. But the great mines of the last century have wrought the most astonishing changes in the landscape. The land above the workings has often subsided at an alarming rate. There were, for instance, severe changes in the valley of the Sankey Brook after 1877, and the London and North-Western Railway, the owners of the Sankey Canal, sued the collieries for damage resulting from 18 feet of subsidence that had taken place in less than a year. In the long corridor of low ground between Wigan and Leigh, subsidence and the disturbance of natural drainage by the mountains of slag have caused the formation of "flashes" (Plate 4 and Fig. 1)—sheets of water frequented today by fishermen and well known to Lancashire field clubs for their abundance of wild life. The miniature mountains of waste from the mines, conical peaks and gullied slopes that look almost like the Red Hills of Skye under certain conditions of light have been nicknamed the Wigan Alps, and are depicted on picture-postcards in the stationers' shops of the district.

The scenery of the coalfield ends in the gentle ridge of sandstone that runs northward for seven miles from Billinge Hill. Even this little ridge, whose outline stands up darkly from the plain in the panoramic view from Rivington Pike, is rich with the material of local history. All along this miniature upland, rising

PLATE 4

The Wigan "flashes" and the Leigh Canal (left). In the distance are the conical slag heaps, known locally as the Wigan Alps.

some 400 feet above the plain, the sandstone of local quarries has given a calm grey unity to the farms and villages.

The western side of the plain is different again. A large part of it lies very near sea level. Close to the Mersey estuary the Triassic sandstone ridges of the Liverpool plateau have been largely overgrown by the city. North of Liverpool a tangle of sand-dunes flanks the coast as far as the Ribble, while inland a series of mosses has been reclaimed to make some of the best agricultural land in the county. Most of this region remained thinly populated until the improvement and settlement of the mosses at the end of the eighteenth century. Although Daniel Defoe looked upon the growth of Liverpool in the time of Queen Anne as one of the wonders of England, its expansion into a metropolitan city only came in the nineteenth century. The same years saw the rise of Southport as a resort amid

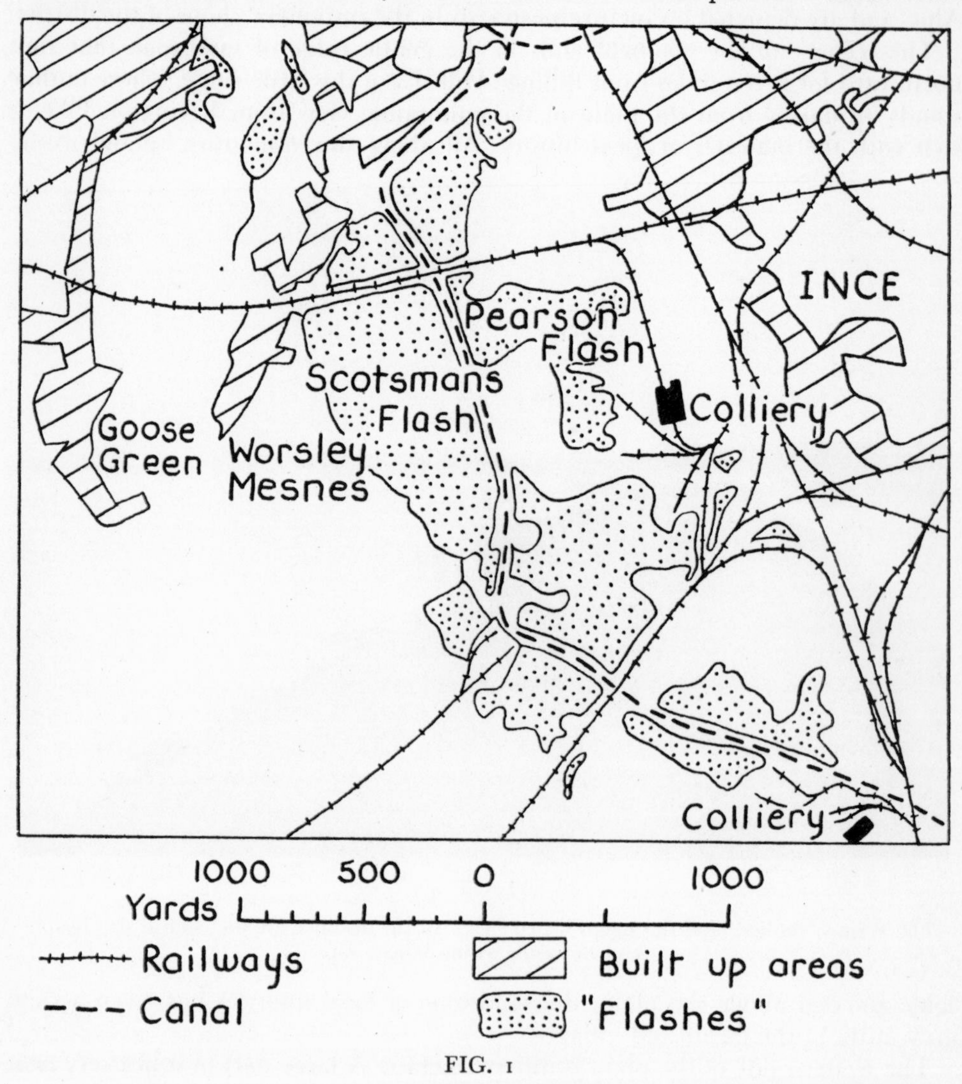

FIG. 1

Ince: the landscape of coal-mining and subsidence. Nearly 250 acres of the township of Ince are under water as a result of subsidence. The Wigan and Leigh Canal, built before the era of deep mining and the consequent blocking of the natural drainage by slag heaps and subsidence, now lies above the level of the "flashes" between embankments.

salt-marshes and sand-dunes, and the creation of St. Helens and Widnes, glass and chemical towns on the fringe of the region. This area has a strong individuality. Among its characteristic features are the huge fields of dark, upchurned soil, the long straight roads that seem to run out right to the horizon, a climate with an unusually large amount of sunshine for North-west England, and many place-names of Norse origin. Its individuality extends to more intangible matters such as a distinct turn and tone of speech, and to a population numbering a high percentage of Roman Catholics, a fact that is explained by the isolation of West Lancashire for a long time after the Reformation and by the heavy Irish immigration of the 1840's.

To the north of the Ribble the plain takes the form of a blunt peninsula—the Fylde. The name means "plain," from the Old English word "gefilde." At the surface it consists of a thick cover of boulder clays with lenses of sand and gravel deposited in the Quaternary Ice Age. Between these low clay hillocks, with their gently curving slopes, the wide depressions were occupied by mosslands—Pilling and Rawcliffe Mosses to the north of the Wyre, and Marton Mere in the long hollow between the squat clay cliffs at Blackpool and the Kirkham ridge. Until their reclamation in the early years of the nineteenth century the mosses were the main cause of the isolation of this district.

On a very clear day the western spurs of Bowland Forest provide a fine panorama of the Fylde. From these moorland summits the plain below looks like a great forest, and it is only the fields at one's feet that show the true nature of this woodland. The "forest" is in fact made up of neat copses and spinneys; the clear green pastures are enclosed with hedges, studded at intervals with oak and ash. It is hard to believe that this rich, stable countryside, which might appear on a brewer's advertisement as a sample of the eternal England, was made only in the past century. Until long after 1800 the Fylde was a grain country, notorious in the eyes of all agricultural improvers. When Holt wrote his *General View of the Agriculture of the County of Lancaster* for the Board of Agriculture in 1795 he complained of the exhausted fields of the Fylde that grew nothing but a succession of oats, barley, and beans. He asserted that some fields in this district had been ploughed without a break for more than a century. "They have undergone the centennial ordeal . . . stock are not largely kept . . . there are no resources of dung, and no large towns or canals to bring it from a distance." With these caustic sentences one of the first surveyors of our agricultural resources suggested some of the changes that were to make the present landscape of the Fylde.

By the 1830's the Fylde was in the course of transformation into a pastoral region. We observe some of the elements in this process in the work of the Duke of Hamilton on his estate at Ashton, just south of Lancaster. In 1838 he formed the Ashton Agricultural Society to spread the knowledge of good farming. He kept a herd of pedigree bulls and along with his cattle-rearing encouraged the cultivation of turnips. In 1845 he opened a tile-works on his estate to make field drains. This was followed in 1847 by the laying of fifty miles of drains, and in 1848 another sixty-two miles. Here is one of the secrets of the green swards that now glisten beneath the clear skies of the Fylde. The Duke of Hamilton also insisted that his tenants should enclose their fields with "thorn fences," planting them with well-spaced deciduous trees. At Ashton and over much of the Fylde the essential features of the landscape were made to the directions of an enlightened and improving landlord.

Northwards again, beyond the river Lune, the plain narrows quickly. It is confined to the seaward end of three peninsulas that project into Morecambe Bay—the Little Fylde, Cartmel, and Furness. Both the geography and the history of the Little Fylde resemble those of the main Fylde to the south of the Lune. The ice sheets that melted away about 20,000 years ago left behind a

PLATE 5

The Ribble valley from Ribchester looking towards Pendle Hill, a lowland of strong Anglian settlement.

hummocky clay plain. On its coast Morecambe has developed as a resort, competing with Blackpool for the holiday traffic of the industrial towns; and Heysham, whose docks and harbour were opened by the Midland Railway Company in 1904, stole the Irish passenger traffic from Fleetwood.

The neighbouring peninsulas of Cartmel and Furness have very different histories. In Cartmel the shapely wooded hills come close to the sea, and the lowland consists of little more than an apron of reclaimed salt-marshes and a ribbon of good soils along the Eea valley. Among the regions of Lancashire,

Cartmel is the most completely aloof. The name is Norse in origin, meaning "sandbank by the rocky ground." Its place-names suggest that the peninsula was only lightly touched by the Anglian settlers of the seventh century and that it long remained an area of refuge for a Celtic population. The parish church of Cartmel, with the upper stage of its square tower curiously set at a diagonal, was one of the very few monastic buildings in Lancashire to escape ruin after the dissolution of the monasteries. And later, apart from the water-powered cotton mill that was opened at Cark in 1782, an eighteenth-century forge at Burblethwaite, and a paper mill, Cartmel was not touched by the Industrial Revolution. The greatest change in the countryside came as a result of the Enclosure Act of 1796, which led to the fencing and hedging of 8,000 acres of common, and the building of over a hundred new roads. Deep drains were cut through the mosses, and embankments constructed to allow the reclamation of the salt-marshes at Wyke and Winder Moor. The Enclosure Act made the landscape of Cartmel as we see it today, creating the patchwork of fields knit together by the thin lines of stone walls and green hedges.

Furness, the remotest part of Lancashire, is largely founded upon the Carboniferous Limestone and the New Red Sandstone, which are covered at the surface by a broken skin of glacial deposits. Both rocks have long provided building stone for barns and farmhouses, for field boundaries and for churches. The sandstone quarries at Hawcoat gave up their warm red rock to the masons who built Furness Abbey between the twelfth and fifteenth centuries, and again in the nineteenth century they provided building-stone for the new steel-town of Barrow.

The mining of the rich iron ores concealed in the Carboniferous limestones forms a continuous thread in the history of Furness. The monks of Furness Abbey manufactured iron and, although there are now no certain remains of their bloomeries, the sites of their ore working and smelting are well known from the entries of the Abbey Coucher Book—a record of the legal and economic affairs of the monastery covering four centuries.[1] Iron bars were one of the prized items of booty carried off by the Scots after their raids on Furness in 1316. Since the beginning of the eighteenth century iron has coloured the history of Furness as vividly as the greasy red ore stained the roads leading from the quarries down to the numerous little ports that then existed along the coast until the trade to South Wales became concentrated on Ulverston and Barrow. In December 1944 iron-mining ceased in Furness. Acres of trenched and upchurned land are now abandoned to the colonizing hawthorn (Fig. 2). Today the basic industry of Furness is only remembered in its place-names. Whitriggs, now a desolate hillside above Dalton, was nicknamed "the Peru of Furness" by Father West in his history of the region published in 1774. "California" records another fabulously wealthy mine of the 1850's.

In any account of the historical development of the Lancashire landscape the

[1] *The Coucher Book of Furness Abbey*, edited by the Rev. J. C. Atkinson and J. Brownbill.

question arises whether a date can be assigned to the beginning of the process. If the modern topographical map be taken as a record of the results of man's transformation of the natural landscape of marsh and moss, moor and woodland, the real beginning should perhaps be dated to the Anglian settlement of Lan-

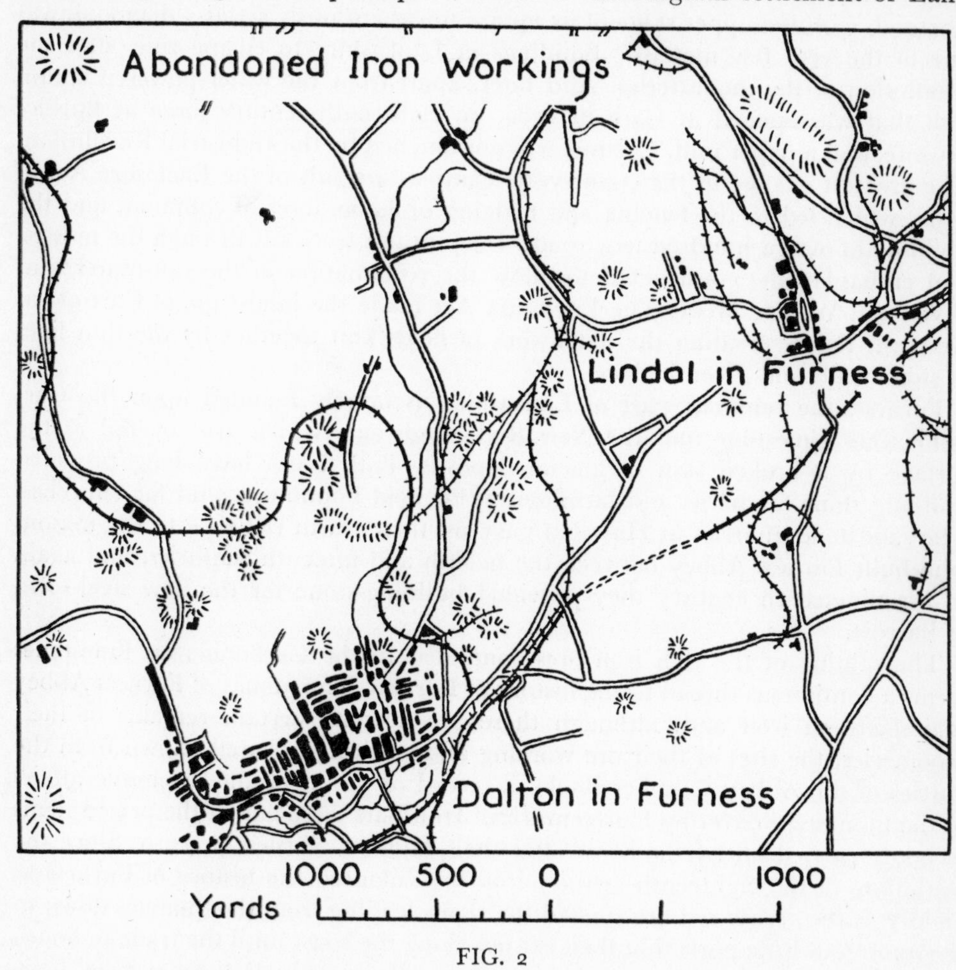

FIG. 2

Furness: abandoned iron-workings near Dalton. The hillsides above Dalton and Lindal bear the scars of iron-mining that came to an end during the Second World War. Dalton was the capital of medieval Furness.

cashire at the close of the sixth century. The Anglo-Saxons planted a large number of village sites in the Lancashire plain, and started an attack on the primitive oakwoods that only came to an end in the early seventeenth century, when the county seems to have been cleared of all its original timber.

Lancashire was never densely settled by early man. This is partly explained by its remote position in north-west England, far from the main centres of population on the chalk and limestone uplands and isolated by the leagues of dense forest that covered the heavy soils of the Midland Plain. Although Lancashire was open to migrants and traders moving northward through the Irish Sea, its coastline seems to have repelled intensive settlement. From the Mersey estuary to Morecambe Bay the coast and the country behind were equally unattractive (Plate 6). Behind the barren sand-dunes or the squat cliffs of boulder clay stretched the mosslands, studded with meres, desolate and uncultivable. Inland again, the

PLATE 6

The coast at Freshfield near Formby. Sand-dunes, advancing inland, have overcome a nineteenth-century plantation.

mosses were succeeded by the heavy clay soils of the plain, covered with thick and tangled woods. On the slopes of the Pennines, and in the hills of Bowland and Rossendale, the great forests gave way to more open woods that reached well above the 1,000-foot contour, possibly covering most of the plateaus which are now occupied by empty, treeless moors and a dark brown skin of blanket-bog.

Only two areas of Lancashire were of any importance in pre-Roman times—the peninsula of Low Furness and the lightly forested slopes and plateaus of the Pennines. Furness contains a long succession of finds to satisfy the archæologist. The chipping-floors of a flint tool factory have been discovered among the sand-dunes at the north end of Walney Island. All but one of the important stone circles of Lancashire can be seen on the Furness hill-tops, while the Iron Age camps at Urswick and on the summit of Warton Crag testify to the importance of the strip of country along the northern rim of Morecambe Bay on the eve of Roman times. Over the rest of Lancashire the record of prehistoric man is neither rich nor interesting. Nowhere in Lancashire can one experience a feeling of contact with the remote past, the indescribable feeling that the centuries of written history are as nothing that comes over one in the shadow of a megalith in distant Cornwall.

Even the Romans left no deep mark on the Lancashire countryside. They made a few roads, mostly centred on Manchester in the extreme south. Some fragments are still used today, while others—like the grooved pavements overgrown with heather on the slopes of Blackstone Edge—have long been abandoned. They established military posts at important sites like Lancaster, Wigan, Manchester and Ribchester. But the complete absence of Roman remains from Furness, and the scarcity of finds from the Fylde and among the marshes and mosses of South-west Lancashire, suggest that this grey rain-soaked plain was only occupied out of military necessity. Yet one cannot completely dismiss the part played by the Romans in the making of Lancashire. Professor Ian Richmond has lately suggested[1] that groups of pensioned soldiers were settled in the Fylde and in the Ribble valley. It is a fascinating thought that troops recruited on the Danube frontier of the Roman Empire began the breaking of the stiff clays of the Lancashire plain.

Certain place-names suggest that some share in the making of the landscape should be assigned to the Celtic people who were still living there when Anglian settlers first penetrated the Pennine valleys. There are many surviving river names of Celtic origin—Ribble, Savock, Cocker, Wyre and Douglas, to mention but a few. Fifty-four place-names in Lancashire contain Celtic elements and, even more significant, the name Makerfield (an early name for the Newton Hundred) seems to belong to a region which might have formed a Celtic enclave. The hills of the south-east also seem to have been a place of refuge for native British well into Anglo-Saxon times.

The sum total of Roman and Celtic influence on the landscape is very small. The process of transforming the wilderness into the landscape we know today begins effectively with the founding of villages from the seventh century onwards. And the most violent impetus in this long process was the Industrial Revolution of the last half of the eighteenth century and the first half of the nineteenth. The growth of scores of towns with close-built streets, jungles of chimney stacks, a labyrinth of railways, roads, and canals, of deserts of mining slag and chemical waste (Plate 7)—all this belongs to the last 200 years, a brief period when a particularly favourable pattern of world trade enabled the bulk of Lancashire people

[1]Richmond, The Sarmatæ and the Regio Bremetennacensis, *The Journal of Roman Studies*, Vol. XXXV (1945).

to divorce themselves from their immemorial countryside. In the following chapters we shall trace in detail how the Lancashire scene, as we have described

PLATE 7

St. Helens: mountains of slag are the only trace of the chemical industry today.

it in the foregoing pages, was slowly shaped and evolved during the space of forty or so human generations that separates us today from the first makers of villages and tillers of the lowland clays.

II

The Countryside

IN the dozen or so generations before the compilation of the Domesday Survey in 1086, two kinds of people settled in Lancashire, and began the making of the landscape. In the last years of the sixth century the Angles penetrated the barrier of the Pennines from their kingdom in Northumbria and reached westward to the Lancashire plain. Another branch of Anglo-Saxon colonists spread northward into Lancashire from the expanding kingdom of Mercia in the seventh century. Ekwall suggests that some of the differences between the dialects of North and South Lancashire are rooted in this early settlement by Northumbrians and Mercians respectively. The "ch" sound that is common in names south of the Ribble (*e.g.*, Man*ch*ester, *Ch*at Moss, *Ch*adderton, Rib*ch*ester) is replaced by the hard "k" in North Lancashire (as in Lancaster), a variation that may spring directly from the original speech differences of Mercian and Northumbrian.

A second great wave of settlers reached Lancashire from across the Irish Sea towards the close of the ninth century. They came from the Norse colonies in Ulster, the Isle of Man, and the Dublin plain. In Lancashire they began the taming of the wastes of the Furness Fells, and settled among the hills that fringe the Lune valley. The abundance of Anglo-Saxon place-names along the floor of the Lune suggests that the Norsemen avoided this ribbon of fertile lowland which had been settled in the previous three centuries. The Fylde seems to have been swamped with Viking farmers, though the name itself is Old English. The Norse language was probably spoken in this part of Lancashire until the twelfth century, and it has entered into many of the place-names and thousands of the minor field-names. Amounderness, the old hundred-name of the Fylde, probably conceals the name of its first Scandinavian overlord, Agmundr. Many of the townships in this region have curious double names. The English "Layton" is joined to the Scandinavian "Warbreck"; the Norse "Westby" is connected with the English "Plumpton." The English farmers were here first, but there were still large empty spaces when the Norsemen arrived.

The Scandinavian immigrants gained another foothold among the desolate sand-dunes and mosses of South-west Lancashire, and the effects of their settlement are clearly written in the pages of Domesday Book. In the hundred of West Derby, twenty-one of the Domesday manors have Scandinavian names, while the remaining thirty are of English origin. Names like Crossens, Kirkby, Scarisbrick, Skelmersdale, date back to the Norse immigration. Even today, when you ride along the straight roads that cleave the huge potato fields around Ormskirk, the names on the signposts have a faintly foreign flavour about them. Ainsdale and Birkdale could just as easily point to some lonely farm in Iceland as to the dormitory suburbs of Manchester's business-men.

Except in the coastal districts Scandinavian place-names are rare in the plain of South Lancashire. They reappear, though with no great density, in the Rossendale upland and on the flanks of the Pennines. Turton embodies a Scandinavian personal name, while Anglezarke, Sholver, Gawkholm, and Brandlesome tell of the settlement of Viking pastoral farmers high among the hills of East Lancashire.

The Scandinavian immigrants were pioneer settlers of the difficult areas which had remained desolate or but thinly populated until the ninth century. Only in Amounderness did the Norsemen settle a region that is among the most fertile and attractive in Lancashire. But even here the presence of forty-six Old English names among the townships and manors of Amounderness shows that the ground-plan of settlement in this region was firmly drawn by the Angles before the appearance of the Norsemen. The double names of townships, the vast number of field-names with Scandinavian elements, the persistence of Norse words like "holm" and "carr" in the living language of today, all point to the permanent and deep impression made by this last great wave of settlers in the Fylde.

The curious shape of the medieval parish of Kirkham may date from the Scandinavian settlement of the Fylde. A detached part of this huge parish used to lie several miles to the east in the broken country at the foot of Beacon Fell. The cattle from the flat lands about Kirkham were sent to these woods and hills for the summer months—a practice that recalls the journey of cattle to the high summer pastures above the Norwegian fiords. This remote part of the medieval parish of Kirkham has now been incorporated in the modern parish of Goosnargh, a tiny hamlet in a region of dispersed farms. The name Goosnargh preserves a faint memory of those Norse farmers driving their cattle to the hills. The ending "argh" goes back to the Old Norse element "erg," meaning a farm on the summer pastures.

The Shapes of Villages

Apart from a few stones with runic inscriptions and the fragments of pre-Norman crosses, the only other tangible reminders of the Angles, Mercians, and Norsemen are the shapes of the villages and hamlets in the Lancashire countryside. They each had distinctive and different ideas about the shapes of their settlements. The Anglo-Saxons lived in large, compact villages (Plate 8), while the Scandinavian place-names are often associated with lonely farms or hamlets of fewer than half a dozen farmsteads.

The shape of the English village has been preserved with great clarity in the parts of Lancashire that escaped the Industrial Revolution. The long village street at Freckleton in the Fylde reproduces a plan that was first sketched before the Norman Conquest. Kirkham is built to the same fundamental design; its central axis, more than a mile long, is crossed at right angles about the middle by another short street lined with buildings. Here the agricultural village, standing amid its open fields, slowly changed its functions after becoming a chartered borough and market town at the end of the thirteenth century. The farms along the village street, surrounded by orchards, gardens, and miniature hedge-enclosed pastures, had given way by the close of the eighteenth century to an unbroken line of warm, brick buildings—the houses of the shopkeepers, the solicitor, and the doctor, and prosperous merchant families like the Langtons, Birleys, and Hornbys, who made their money out of the flax and cotton mills.

Close to Liverpool several villages whose names appear in the Domesday Survey have been entangled in the great expansion of the city since 1800. Domesday Book tells us that "Dot held Hitune and Torboc." Huyton has now lost all its roots in the countryside. Even in 1880 *Murray's Handbook of Lancashire* was able

PLATE 8

Warton: a nucleated Anglian settlement at the foot of a limestone crag. It received a borough charter in the thirteenth century but was still a village of farmers, set amid its common fields, when Lucas wrote his parish history between 1710 and 1744.

to write "of late years Huyton has become a favourite residence for Liverpool merchants." Today it is surrounded by the vast municipal housing estates built by the Liverpool Corporation between two world wars. Only the church, an eleventh-century foundation, and the site of the village street (now part of a busy road into Liverpool) serve to remind us of the distant origins of this Anglo-Saxon village.

Several nucleated villages are found in the lowland of Plain Furness, commemorating in their plan the Anglian settlement of this peninsula. Great Urswick is gathered neatly along the shore of its placid tarn. Its parish church of St. Mary's in the Fields dates from the thirteenth century, but the fragments of two tenth-century crosses support the idea that there was a church and a village community in existence at Urswick well before the Norman Conquest. This was one of the first churches in Furness. It later became the mother church to Pennington and Ulverston, giving strength to the view that this was one of the primary Anglian settlements in Furness.

There are few surviving examples in the Lancashire plain of the "green" villages that are so common in lowland England and on the other side of the Pennines in Northumberland and Durham. Lancashire formerly had many more village greens, but a considerable number have disappeared within the past 200 years, having been enclosed with or without statutory order. The hundred or so "green" villages of Durham are largely a product of the Anglian settlement and probably a direct intrusion into England of a settlement-form that is widespread on the plains of Germany and Denmark. Wrea Green has the largest surviving village green in Lancashire. Leece in Furness is an example of a settlement focused on a central green.

The long Anglo-Saxon street-village is replaced by an entirely different form of settlement in the areas colonized by the Scandinavians. The small clusters of farms in the Furness Fells and the hamlets that lie between 500 and 1,200 feet above sea level on the Pennine slopes are characteristic of these tenth-century settlers. Sholver stands on the hills above Oldham's forest of chimney stacks. This grey ring of cottages and farms betrays its origin by its name and shape. It is "the *erg* of a farmer called Skjolgr," a name that takes us back a thousand years to the time when some Scandinavian farmer first cleared the ground for a summer shieling on these bleak, rain-soaked hills. The plan of the hamlet has probably changed little since the early Middle Ages, although none of the buildings in modern Sholver date back to a time before the end of the seventeenth century, when, in an age of reconstruction, the medieval timber and plaster were replaced by solid farms in the local grey sandstone. Despite this change the sites of the buildings in the hamlet have remained substantially the same. The cottages and barns are still grouped around a wide central green (Plate 9). A century ago the fields around Sholver were worked by several yeomen farmers who lived in the hamlet. The freehold of these farms had been bought from the Prestwich family in the seventeenth century, at the time when the settlement was largely rebuilt in stone. Butterworth in his *Historical Sketches of Oldham* (1849) records that in 1752 Top o' th' Fold, Sholver, was owned by John Kershaw, "an opulent freeholder." A great change came over the hill farms of East Lancashire in the nineteenth century when many adventurous yeomen began to invest their capital in the rising industries of Oldham. For instance, the Lees family, who became the greatest cotton spinners in Oldham, descended from a stock of yeomen farmers. The family took its name from the hamlet where they purchased the freehold of their land in 1625. Today the pastoral hamlet of Lees has become deeply embedded in Oldham. Narrow streets and tall gloomy mills have displaced the meagre fields. Sholver has escaped such complete physical destruction, but the blight of the Industrial Revolution has deeply affected the life of the hamlet. The individual holdings were gradually absorbed by Sholver farm as yeomen families drifted away to try their luck in the boom-and-slump economy of the cotton towns. For several years the grey seventeenth-century house of Sholver farm has stood empty, slowly being beaten into a ruin by winter gales and children's games. The lands of what was once a free community of small farmers belong to a farm that lies half a mile away down the steep lane to Heyside.

Among the Furness Fells the pattern of the original Norse settlement remains much clearer than it does in South-east Lancashire, where many of the hamlets have been swallowed by the spreading industrial towns. High Furness has one of

PLATE 9

Sholver ("the *erg* of a farmer called Skjolgr") began as a Norse summer shieling on the moors above Oldham. The stone-built farms preserve the circular shape of an ancient village green.

the most attractive landscapes in the British Isles. The valleys that lie between the folds of its little hills are clothed with copses of oak, hazel, and birch. Apart from the small town of Hawkshead, the normal pattern of settlement in High Furness is the close-compacted hamlet of a few farms. The "thwaite" element, derived from the Old Norse for a clearing, repeats itself in the name of almost every hamlet, as in Satterthwaite, Finsthwaite, Haverthwaite. These were the primary settlements of High Furness from which a long, slow process of expansion and clearance was carried on through the Middle Ages right down into the sixteenth century (Fig. 3).

In his fine history of Hawkshead, Cowper shows how the society of the hamlets of High Furness kept its individuality for many centuries. Dialect words and the forms of late medieval place-names show that a Scandinavian language was spoken until long after the Norman Conquest. The element "ground" is frequently found in the names of farms that were created from the waste at the beginning of the sixteenth century. Around Hawkshead we find Sand Ground, Sawrey Ground, and Kendall Ground. The same element commonly appears as a farm-name in Iceland with the word "grund." Among the field-names recorded in the Coucher Book of Furness Abbey, some are so strongly Scandinavian that they almost defy pronunciation. For instance, we find *Stodfaldwra* and *Rotherisat* among the minor names. The hamlets were each inhabited by members of the same family, and Cowper thought that they may have started as single farmsteads to which new buildings were added as the family developed into something as complex as a clan. Even as recently as a hundred years ago, or a little more, the chief families of High Furness were thickly grouped in districts around particular hamlets. The Turners lived near the large hamlet of Oxenpark, the Taylors at Finsthwaite, and the Satterthwaites in the neighbourhood of the settlement of the same name.

As one travels through High Furness today it is easy to gain the impression that this countryside has scarcely passed beyond the stage of its first clearance and primary settlement. The hamlets crouch in their narrow valleys, surrounded by a patchwork of small pastures and shut in by dense copses of hazel and birch. The whole scene is framed with a heath, stained with the browns and purple of heather and the dull summer greens and bright winter chrome of bracken. But this impression of a half-wild landscape is an illusion. The woods were planted in the eighteenth century to satisfy the demand for charcoal in the Furness iron industry and the hill-top moors have been modified through centuries of grazing by large flocks of sheep.

Medieval Colonization

The Norman Conquest marks the end of the long period in which colonists had reached the British Isles from Europe. The distribution of the manors and estates of North-west England among the followers of William the Conqueror led to the creation of Lancashire as we know it. The county arose out of the lands that were given to Count Roger of Poitou, and its boundaries were drawn some time between 1086 and 1090. The Domesday Survey of 1086 shows no knowledge of Lancashire as a unit. The region south of the Ribble, "inter Rippam et Mersham," is included with Cheshire, while the rest of the county is entered under Yorkshire. In 1102 Count Roger's estates, called the Honour of Lancaster, were confiscated by Henry I. They consisted of scattered and valuable manors in Lincolnshire, Leicestershire, Essex, and Derbyshire, but Count Roger's main possessions formed a block of territory in North-west England, including Furness, Cartmel, the parish of Warton, which had previously been part of Kendal, Amounderness and the lands south of the Ribble—substantially the modern Lancashire.

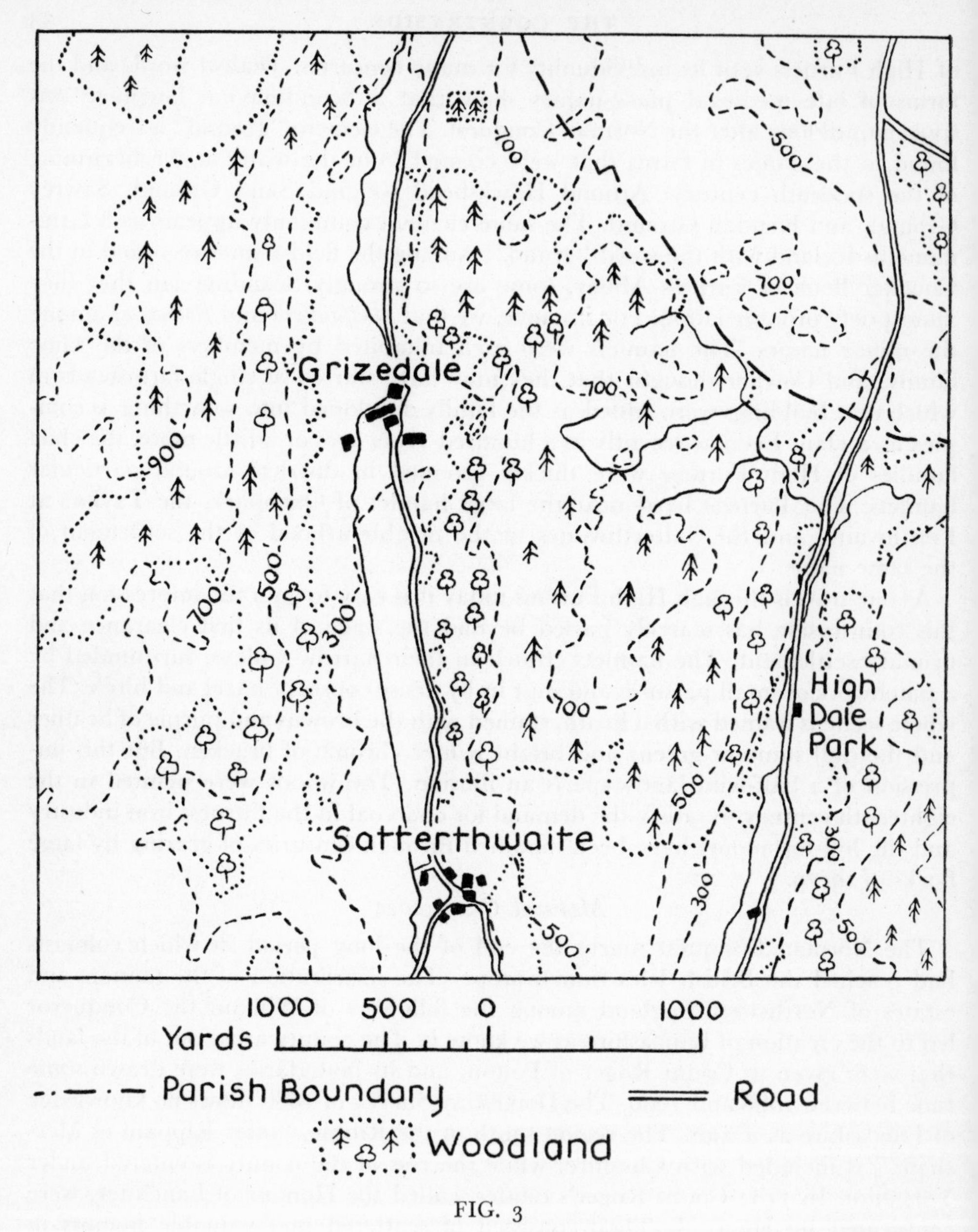

FIG. 3

High Furness: Medieval hamlet settlement. Satterthwaite and Grizedale are hamlets of Norse origin. High Dale Park commemorates the conversion of a large tract of country into a deer park in 1516 by Abbot Alexander Banke.

For most English counties, Domesday Book is the starting-point of any detailed study of the local history and topography; but the survey for Lancashire is meagre and disappointing, and we are left in the dark about important questions that affect our study of the landscape. All we can say is that by the closing years of the eleventh century most of the villages of the Lancashire plain were firmly established, surrounded in all probability by their own open fields cultivated in the traditional manner. The hill-country was still largely a forested waste up to a thousand feet or more, and above that lay the bleak, open moorland. Even in the lowlands some places are still not recorded in Domesday Book. We do not hear of Ormskirk as a name until more than a hundred years later (1196), or of Liverpool until just about the same date (1194). The absence of a particular place-name from Domesday is not absolute proof of a later origin, for all over England we find large manors (royal and episcopal manors especially) which silently include many other places round about, some of which we know from Anglo-Saxon charters had already existed for many generations. We have, therefore, to be careful how we interpret the silences of Domesday Book.

It seems likely, however, that no settlement existed on the shores of the tidal creek (now filled up) at Liverpool. Not until the closing years of the twelfth century—one of the most formative periods in the history of the English landscape—do we hear of traders and fishermen settling by the shores of the turgid and clotted pool (the Old English word for "clotted" is *lifrig*) that gave its name to the original village and thence to the great city that we know today. Ormskirk, similarly, may not have come into existence until the time of Henry II, but of that we cannot be so sure.

What we do know is that by 1086—some 400 years after the first Anglian colonists had penetrated into what we now call Lancashire—the population of the county was still no more than seven or eight thousand all told. There were fewer people in Lancashire in 1086 than in little Huntingdonshire at the same date, and only about half as many as there were in Bedfordshire. Or, to put it in another way, there were in the whole of Lancashire at the end of the eleventh century about half as many people as in the urban district of Ramsbottom today, and just about as many as in the rural districts of Lunesdale or Clitheroe. Nothing could illustrate more vividly how little had yet been done to tame and humanize the natural landscape of Lancashire, how thinly people were still spread over the great lonely countryside that stretched between the Mersey and the Furness Fells —a distance of more than seventy miles—and how much of the landscape still silently awaited the fire and axe of the first medieval colonists.

When the Domesday place-names are studied together with those of later date the course of medieval colonization begins to emerge. For instance, the countryside on the fringe of Liverpool contains a mixture of nucleated villages and of dispersed townships whose only centre is a hamlet with a public-house, a post office, and a parish church. Hale and Halewood, now on the edge of Liverpool's expanding suburbs, illustrate this process of post-Domesday colonization with great clarity. Hale was a primary Anglo-Saxon settlement and is recorded in Domesday Book. It is impressively situated on a low ridge projecting into the

Mersey estuary. Eastward from the village one looks up the river to the shapely sandstone hills about Runcorn and across the dreary Ditton marshes, littered with the apparatus of one of the biggest chemical works in the country. Westward lies the Mersey's broad and beautiful inner estuary, its mudflats and channels changing shape with every tide; beyond are the soap mills, oil refineries, and residential suburbs along the low coast of Wirral. To the north of Hale stretches a countryside of quiet lanes and isolated farms in which the most important settlement is Halewood, scarcely more than a few houses standing at a cross-road. The name itself first appears in the Cockersand Cartulary at the beginning of the thirteenth century. It was situated in the "wood belonging to Hale," a wilderness that had been slowly colonized since Domesday times from the parent village by farmers who made clearings in the forest and established their isolated holdings.

Knowsley was a similar clearance in the band of woodland that once covered the eastern part of the Liverpool plateau. It means "the clearing of Cynewulf," and keeps fresh the memory of one of the many individuals who first burnt the forest and grubbed up the deep-rooted trees to make a farm in lowland Lancashire.

The place-names of East Lancashire reveal a notable colonization of the bleak uplands of Rossendale and Pendle in the late Middle Ages. The settlers moved into the high moorland valleys from the neighbouring, long-occupied lowlands and took up cattle-farming. This movement is clearly illustrated by a comparison of the place-names along the fertile valleys of the Ribble and Calder and in the bordering hill-masses of Pendle and Rossendale. The Anglo-Saxon "ton" and "ham" elements are common in the names of valley settlements (as in Mitton, Pendleton, Twiston, Worston, and Padiham), where they point to villages established before the Norman Conquest. The suffix "ley," generally a sign of late colonization and slow forest-clearance, abounds in the place-names of the uplands. The hill place-names often contain allusions to cattle-rearing and crops. In the Forest of Pendle we find late names like "Barley," "Wheatley," and "Ryley," while Studley and Calverley recall the cattle-rearing that was the main occupation of upland Lancashire in the Middle Ages. Striking proof is added to this argument by a study of the township names in the tax assessments of 1327-1332. Of the forty-seven townships in the vast medieval parish of Whalley only twenty-seven are recorded in this document. By contrast the township names of long-settled areas (like the lowland hundred of Salford) are nearly complete in the assessments.

Several villages in Rossendale and occasionally an individual farm can be dated back to the establishment of these medieval cattle-ranches. The manorial accounts of this district in the Honour of Clitheroe show that these specialized cattle-farms were founded in the latter half of the thirteenth century. By the end of the century eleven "vaccaries" are recorded in the Forest of Pendle.

In Rossendale the disafforestation order of 1507 contains a list of the cattle-farms then existing. Among the names are Rawtenstall, Constable Lee, and

Crawshaw Booth. Today these are industrial towns and villages—their cotton mills and slipper works packed into the narrow valley of the Limey Water. At the head of the same valley, and at almost a thousand feet above sea level, three other settlements first came into existence as cattle-farms in the thirteenth century. Since that time they have gone their different economic ways. Love Clough, a grey hamlet and a mill, stands astride the Limey Water. Dunnockshaw has given its name to a drab row of stone cottages on the main road from Rawtenstall to Burnley. Gambleside survived as a farm until it was abandoned a few years ago. Today the name belongs to a heap of stones on the edge of Dunnockshaw reservoir.

The history of settlement in Rossendale enters a new phase with the abolition of the Forest Laws by Henry VII. The removal of this legal barrier led to the clearance and improvement of waste land. New settlers were attracted to the region and the large cattle-farms began to disintegrate into small pastoral holdings. At the same time the haphazard and mainly unrecorded enclosure of small patches of land from the moorland was going on. The Clitheroe manor court rolls preserve a few of the details of this piecemeal invasion of the wastes of Rossendale. This record shows that in 1538 two landless settlers, John and Ambrose Fenton, were fined fourpence "for encroaching a certain parcel of the King's waste in the vill of Haslingden, and thereon settling a house, without licence."[1]

The settlement of Rossendale continued throughout the seventeenth and eighteenth centuries with the influx of migrants from the neighbouring lowlands, who started the textile industry here. The manufacture of woollen cloth, and later cotton, in the countryside of Rossendale seems to have had the effect of breaking up the larger farms, of increasing the number of smallholdings. A comparison of a rental of 1662 with a similar survey made in 1608 shows a 50 per cent. increase in the number of separately rented pieces of land. In the seventeenth century Rossendale became a region of small farms, each keeping a cow or two, a few sheep, and a hencote, where a living was eked out by selling the products of the loomshop in the markets at Rochdale and Manchester.

The results of three centuries of colonization in Rossendale are clearly visible in the contemporary landscape. The high bare moors that fill the scene in the upper tributaries of the Irwell are dotted with small, isolated farms, some lying as high as the 1,250-foot contour. Many now stand in ruins as a result of the retreat of farming from the uplands during the past seventy years (Plate 10). By contrast, the moors to the east of Burnley, which lay outside the boundary of Rossendale Forest, escaped the stream of squatters who broke the soil up to such inhospitable heights. They remained in the control of estates which prevented their colonization, and today much of the high land still stands as untamed grouse-moor.

The rising population of Rossendale after the disafforestation led to the building of chapels and the creation of new parishes. A chapel was built at Newchurch in 1511 and, as an order of the Court of the Duchy of Lancaster states, "was made

[1] G. H. Tupling, *The Economic History of Rossendale*, 57 ff.

parochial by King Edward VI and called by the name of the chapel of our Saviour, with a parcel of ground enclosed with a hedge, called the Chapel Yard, to have all offices performed in it as in any other parish church. . . ." The disafforestation of Pendle at the same time as Rossendale similarly brought about the creation of new townships and parishes. The broken country on the southern flank of this high table-like moorland was divided into a number of townships that took their names from the medieval cattle-farms. They include Old Laund Booth, Goldshaw Booth, and Rough Lee Booth. The name Newchurch recurs in this district and belongs to a chapel that was erected in Goldshaw Booth about the year 1529. Newchurch-in-Pendle escaped the industrialism that choked the

PLATE 10

An abandoned farm in Rossendale, over 1,000 feet above sea level: one of many that have gone out of cultivation since 1870.

Irwell at Newchurch-in-Rossendale with grim stone mills. It is still little more than a cross-road hamlet in a quiet countryside.

A few miles to the west of Pendle Hill, beyond the Ribble and its tributary Hodder, the map reveals an interesting piece of country. Between the Ribble and the southern outlier of Bowland Forest at Calder Fell is a countryside strongly reminiscent of deepest Devon: a close tangle of winding lanes (Plate 11), an almost complete absence of villages beyond Longridge, and a thick powdering of isolated farmsteads with a rare hamlet such as Bleasdale. All this suggests, to the observant eye, country which has been reclaimed acre by acre from the aboriginal waste by colonists coming from older settlements in the lower country, colonists who enclosed their little pastoral farms directly from the waste and occupied them in separate ownership from the first, just as they did in pastoral Devon at the same period. These farms were named after the predominant trees in the woods—

Ashes, Oakenclough, Hazelhurst, and Birchen Lee. Occasionally there is a name that records more vividly the lonely hazards of these medieval pioneers on the fell-side, such as Wolfen Hall below Wolf Fell (Fig. 4).

And in this country, too, is a place-name that excites our curiosity by its very unexpectedness. It is Chipping, applied today to a remote little place hardly bigger than a hamlet, but a name indicating a medieval market or market town; and it gives us a clue perhaps to the otherwise unrecorded process of colonization on the southern foothills of Bowland Forest. For Chipping is first recorded as a name in the year 1203. A market must have existed here at that early date, and

PLATE 11

Balderstone in the Ribble valley: the winding lane and small irregular fields are characteristic of medieval clearance from woodland.

it surely reflects an advanced stage in the process of creating new fields and farms, when the work of settlement and taming the wilds had gone far enough to warrant the setting up of a market, however small, to gather in the surplus produce of these pastoral hillside farms. Over the shoulder of the moor the hamlet of Bleasdale lies about 200 feet higher on a more exposed slope, and is first recorded by name in 1228. It seems evident that this country between the Ribble and Calder Fell, forested in its natural state, was being actively colonized and its landscape fashioned during the latter part of the twelfth century and the early years of the thirteenth. But these early settlers, though they founded new farms all over the

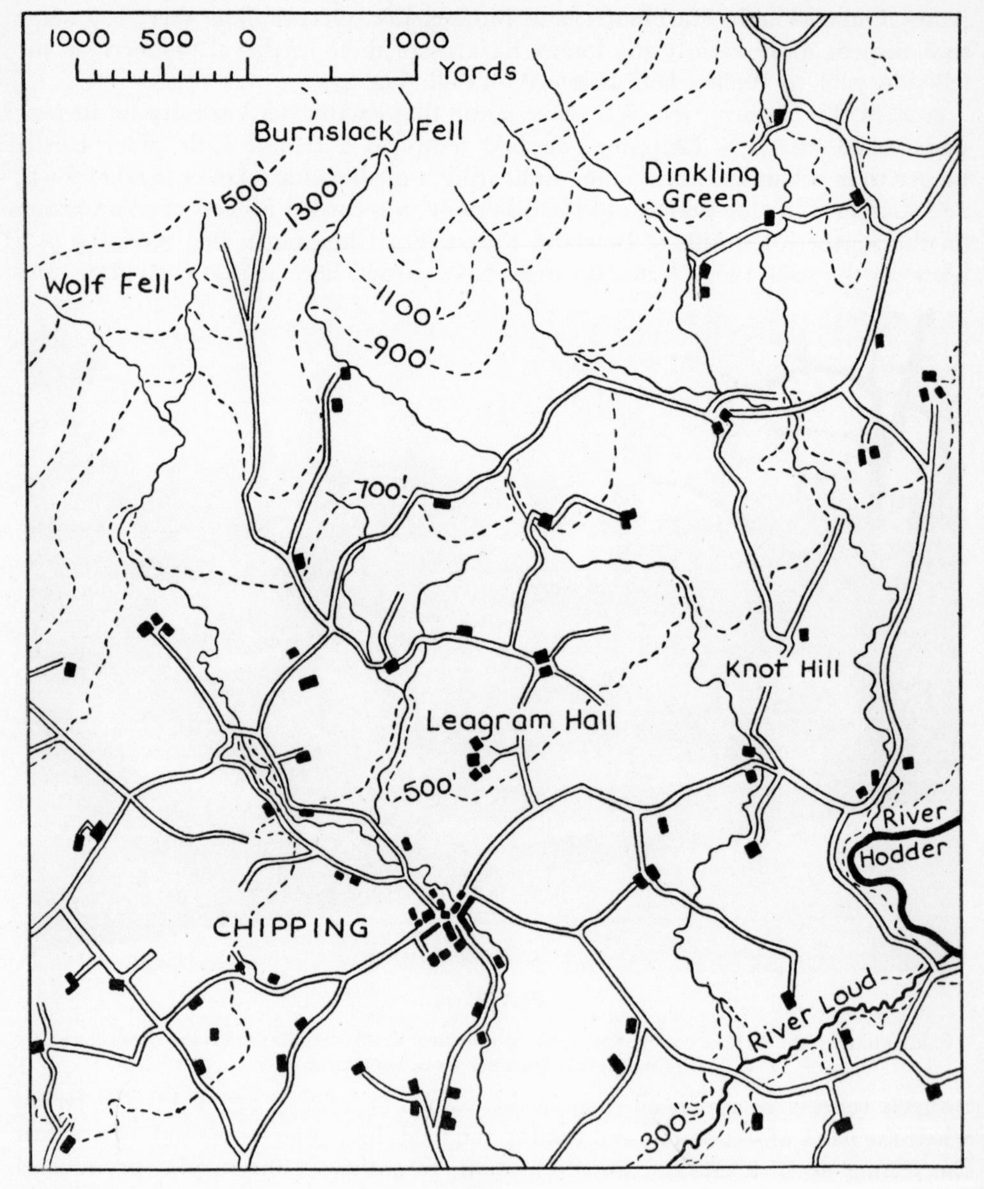

FIG. 4

Bowland Forest: a landscape of medieval colonization. Note the dispersed farmsteads and the network of winding lanes.

slopes, still left much waste untouched between and above the farms, and the process of reclamation was not to be completed for many centuries.

Medieval Furness

A study of the development of the Furness peninsula in the Middle Ages reveals yet another factor in the shaping of the landscape, and that is the influence of monastic houses deliberately planted in the wilds, above all the Cistercian houses. In 1127, as a result of a gift of land to the Norman abbey of Savigny, a daughter monastery was founded in Beckang's Gill, a sheltered valley on the outskirts of Dalton. Even since its invasion by the railway and the crowds of summer trippers Furness Abbey still gives an impression of quiet beauty. In 1163 the monks added

PLATE 12

An isolated farm near Broughton in High Furness. Dry stone walls form the field boundaries and climb the hillside to the moorland edge.

the Furness Fells to their territory; within two more generations they controlled the whole peninsula.

The possessions of the Abbey included two vastly different types of country: Plain Furness, a fertile lowland rich in iron ore, and High Furness, a poor hill-country best fitted for sheep farming. Under the rule of the monastery the relations between High and Plain Furness resembled those between a colony and its mother-country.

The period of monastic colonization is commemorated in the names of farms in the Furness Fells, where the "parks" and "grounds" represent two stages of medieval settlement and economic improvement. The "park" names may date from almost any time between the twelfth century and the Reformation. They represent the enclosure of open fell or the clearance of woodland for sheep runs. The constant references in medieval documents to "parks" and "granges," the farms owned by the Abbey and worked by a class of monks as "converts," show that the creation of sheepwalks in the fells reached its greatest height in the fourteenth century. In High Furness, Lawson Park and Parkamoor, lonely sheep-farms above Coniston Water, stand today on the sites of former granges of Furness Abbey.

The "parks" that lie south of Hawkshead along the pleasant valley of Dale Park Beck—High Dale Park, Middle Dale Park, and Low Dale Park—have a different origin. They commemorate the conversion of a large tract of Grizedale into a deer park by Abbot Alexander Banke in 1516. Abbot Banke seems to have ruled his little kingdom with a ruthlessness worthy of a Renaissance prince. In addition to the enclosure of Grizedale with a fence five miles in length, he created another great deer park, the New Park, at the western gate of Furness Abbey. It was seven miles "compass about" and involved the destruction of a whole village, Sellergarth, and the eviction of its thirty-two tenants and their families. Today there is no trace of the village apart from a brief reference in the Pleadings of the Duchy of Lancaster, where we read of a complaint that "the Abbot had pulled down the whole town of Sellergarth, which had 32 tenements, and had laid a third of it to pasture." Its probable site has been preserved in the name of a field, Sellar Butts, which lies near to the western gateway of Furness Abbey.

The farm-names ending in "ground" belong to a wave of enclosure that took place in High Furness at the beginning of the sixteenth century. Thirty-six of these names can be counted in the region, and most of them bear the name of the family responsible for their patch of improvement from the waste (for instance, Sawrey Ground, Thompson Ground, and Kendall Ground). The story of the creation of these small farms can be traced, however barely, in two agreements signed between the Abbey and its tenants at Colton and Hawkshead Hall in 1509 and 1532 respectively. No doubt these documents tell of an effort by the abbot to control the enclosure that had been going on for many years and which resulted in the building of new farms at the expense of the natural woodland and common pasture. The agreement of 1509 allowed the enclosure of 1½ acres of "such ground as hath been of the common pasture within the time of man's mind." The tenant, who was practically a freeholder, was not to go beyond these limits, and his property had "to be hedged with a dyke or wall." Here is evidence that some of the field boundaries around the hamlets of High Furness can be dated to the late Middle Ages. The fells above the beautiful narrow valleys remained as vast open sheep walks for another three centuries until they were enclosed and ribbed with dark slate walls.

The day in 1537 when the last Abbot of Furness, Roger Pele, surrendered "all his interest in the house and lands of Furness Abbey to the King" was as important in the history of this region as the disafforestation of the hills of East Lancashire thirty years earlier. Within a few weeks the great abbey was turned into the ruin that centuries later made it a centre of attraction for Victorian antiquarians and the followers of the Gothic revival. On 23 June, 1537, the Receiver, Robert Southwell, arrived at the abbey to dismiss the monks and wind up its affairs. Within a fortnight the church had been unroofed, and the lead stripped from the roofs of most of the other buildings to be melted down and cast into pigs imprinted with the King's mark. For years after its destruction Furness Abbey served as a quarry for building stone that was used over a large part of Plain Furness. The hewn blocks of red sandstone, often with elaborate decoration, turn up in humble farm buildings in the neighbourhood of Dalton. Stone from the abbey was used to rebuild Ulverston parish church in 1540 after a severe gale had brought down the steeple and "utterly destroyed" the chancel. The Duchy Pleadings of that time tell how King Henry VIII issued instructions to use the building materials from the abandoned monasteries. "The King, in a reply to a petition of the inhabitants and parishioners, commanded them to take stones convenient for the rebuilding of the chancel at our manors and late monasteries of Furness and Conishead" . . . "there were enough stones at Furness to build five or six churches."

The destruction of Furness Abbey caused the rise to wealth and power of the "statesmen," the yeomen farmers who took over much of the monastery's land. This class of small free landowners sprang from the customary tenants who won the right to carve their farms out of the woods and fells of High Furness at the beginning of the sixteenth century. By 1586, when Elizabeth issued a code of laws for the district, the statesmen were confirmed as the most powerful group in Furness.

Rebuilding in Stone

The prosperity of the statesmen shows itself in the latter half of the seventeenth century with a great wave of rebuilding. Most of the farmhouses of High Furness date from the period between 1650 and 1710. The new house was often built on the foundations of the old one. A "statesman" family built Borwick Lodge at Hawkshead on the site of Borwick Ground, a farm that had been created early in the sixteenth century. Hawkshead Hall, which started as a "grange" of Furness Abbey, was largely rebuilt in the seventeenth century by the Nicholson family, so that today a whitewashed farm stands behind the dark fragment of a medieval gatehouse (Plate 13).

The new farms were largely built of blue-grey slate, the most common local material, and are usually planned with the stable and barn under the same roof-line as the house. The outside walls of the dwelling quarters were plastered with a lime rough-cast to make them wind and weather proof. Today this style of building forms the most characteristic feature of the countryside of High Furness. The long, low farms, cowering against the rising ground of the fell, stand out from afar off as a splash of dazzling white against the grey-green pastures and the brilliant orange-chrome slopes of dead bracken in the early spring.

Furness slate is one of the most unsatisfactory building materials in Lancashire. The thin slabs always seem to keep an ugly sharp edge, and they cannot be worked into shapes or decorated. As a result, there are few date-stones on the farm buildings of the Hawkshead district. The plain rough-cast fronts and blue

PLATE 13

The gatehouse of Hawkshead Hall: the only fragment of medieval Hawkshead, a Norse settlement (the shieling of Hawkr) that became a grange of Furness Abbey.

slate barns might belong to any part of the last four centuries. Cowper in his history of Hawkshead suggests that the most satisfactory way of dating these buildings is through the inscriptions and dates on the huge oak bread cupboards that are part of the structure in a Furness farm. Most of them fall into the latter part of the seventeenth century and the early years of the eighteenth century.

The wave of rebuilding in stone was not confined to Furness. We find that the yeomen-farmers of the rest of Lancashire largely rebuilt their homes between the middle of the sixteenth century and the start of the eighteenth century. In South-east Lancashire the reconstruction of farms started more than a century before the same movement in Furness, a fact that may be attributed to the capital created by the penetration of this district by industry. Stubley Old Hall, near Rochdale, was rebuilt by Robert Holt in 1529, and he used stone and brick to replace a timber-framed house. Dr. Whitaker, the Lancashire antiquarian of the late eighteenth century, claimed that this was the "first instance of an entire hall-house of brick and stone."

In the large parish of Burnley most of the old farmhouses were rebuilt from the last quarter of the sixteenth century onwards. Mr. Bennett,[1] in his admirable history of Burnley, gives us a detailed picture of this change in the human scene, a change that must have been equally evident in most of the upland parishes where stone was plentiful. "Evidence of the increasing wealth of Burnley," he says, "is the widespread activity in house-building, particularly by the richer inhabitants. Towneley, Gawthorpe (1600), Royle (about 1600), Rowley (1593), Barcroft (1614), Heasandford (about 1600), Fulledge (1576), Extwistle (about 1580: rear wing 1637), and Greenhill (about 1600), were remodelled or rebuilt to suit the larger purses of the more prosperous owners, while Danes House, Lodge Farm, and many others show the same tendency among 'substantial' farmers. The new type of farmhouse was stone-built, with one, two, or three bays, mullioned windows, and sturdy oak door. The hall, which was used as the main living room, was generally entered by a porch, and had a parlour at one end, and kitchen, buttery, and storehouses at the other end. Wide, open chimneys with their inglenooks provided ample space for the whole family to enjoy the warmth from a blazing log. Bedrooms, reached by a stone staircase, were to be found in all the newer houses. Often the farmstead was built in a little valley or sheltered behind a slight ridge. If possible, it faced north and east, for it was thought that the north wind was a 'preservative from corruption,' and that the east wind brought bright, serene weather"—a rare feature of the Lancashire climate in the late spring and early summer. "Barns and shippons were usually erected at some distance from the house, which now looked on a pleasant garden instead of the less pleasantly scented farmyard. In small farms, however, the old custom of building the barn next to the house was maintained." In this manner, and at this time, were born those very characteristic stone farmhouses that one still sees dotted about the more remote parishes in the folds of the hills. Wherever one sees them, they may generally be dated to the generation before or after 1600, when the yeomen and the small gentry were at their most prosperous (Plate 14).

Some of these houses have survived in the sordid hearts of the big industrial towns. Clegg Hall, close to Rochdale, is a good sample of a manor house that has been degraded by industry. The first mention of the estate appears in the early thirteenth century, when the Towneley transcripts record that Hugh de Clegg granted a piece of land to his brother Ivo. The present house, its harsh grey stone blackened by the smoke of Rochdale's mills, was put on the site of an earlier

[1] Bennett, *The History of Burnley*, Part II, 64, 240.

building some time about the turn of the sixteenth century. By the end of Victoria's reign Clegg Hall had been converted into tenements. It offered no attractions as a home to the wealthy manufacturers of Rochdale who had destroyed all the amenities of this part of the Roch valley by their own industry. The Rochdale Canal spreads its dirty opaque ribbon beneath the windows of Clegg Hall; the main line of the Lancashire and Yorkshire Railway runs a few yards away across the fields; and beyond are the cotton mills of Smallbridge.

The date-stones cut by some rural artisan and the colourless sentences of legal

PLATE 14

The manor-house at Downham: an example of the rebuilding in stone that went on in the seventeenth century among the hills of East Lancashire.

documents provide the main evidence for the building of comfortable farmhouses all over the Lancashire countryside in the sixteenth and seventeenth centuries. Apart from a vivid page in the diary of Adam Martindale we know little about the details of the rebuilding and the feelings of their owners about the new house. Adam Martindale was born at Moss Bank, now almost caught up in the northern suburbs of St. Helens, in 1623. He lived through the Civil War and became a nonconformist minister. His diary opens with memories of his early childhood—the sight of "the open eye" of a coal pit near St. Helen's chapel and an escape from drowning in a marl pit. There is an account of his birthplace. "The particular place of my birth was at the High-Heyes, by Mossebanke, in that prettie neat habitation called the new house (in opposition to the old one then standing), which father first built and annexed to his newe barne, from which in time, when the whole tenemente was his own, he removed to the old house, pullinge downe the inner walls, floores and chimnies, of the new one, and laying it to the barne, to furnish him with more stowage for his corne. And in the processe of time he, together with my brother Thomas, pulled downe the olde house quite to the ground, and built that strong and large stone house that now stands in its place." In his own lifetime Adam Martindale's father built two new farmhouses; the second "strong and large stone house" on the exact site of its medieval predecessor after he had become richer with the addition of fresh land to his estate.

Lancashire's yeomen farmers have not only left their mark on the landscape in scores of solid farm buildings, but they contributed to the foundation of many grammar schools. Edwin Sandys, Archbishop of York, and a member of a famous Furness family, obtained letters patent for the foundation of Hawkshead Grammar School in 1585. Upholland Grammar School, which was opened in 1661, clearly owes its origin to the yeomen-farmers of the district. Its history begins in 1656 when Richard Leigh, a member of a family that had grown wealthy out of the dissolution of the lands of Upholland Priory, gave the western part of Mickleholme Meadows into the care of trustees. The rent of this was to contribute to the upkeep of a schoolmaster. Richard Leigh died in 1658 and his will provided Milnehey Meadow as a building site for the school. At the same time a school stock was established and every yeoman in the district was asked to contribute a fixed sum towards it. Many of these deeds are still in existence and contain names, like the Gaskells, Ashursts, and Rigbys, that have been common in the registers of the school right down to the present day.

The Landscape of Enclosure

Perhaps the most ubiquitous features of the Lancashire landscape are the hedges, earth banks, stone fences, and open mortarless walls that form the field boundaries in both the plain and the bleak uplands (Plate 15). They seem such a natural part of the scenery that one scarcely questions their origin. Yet these fences form one of the most vital items in the transformation of the countryside.

It is difficult to discover the date of the first enclosures. It has already been suggested that on the lower slopes below Calder Fell they may go back to the twelfth century, and similarly in Furness also. Some of the earliest documentary references come from the first half of the fourteenth century, and it is clear that from 1300 until the close of the nineteenth century the process was almost continuous. By 1700 most of the open arable fields in the county had been transformed into small hedged enclosures. When Holt wrote his *General View* for the Board of Agriculture in 1795 he calculated that 482,000 acres of Lancashire consisted of open moor and common. He recommended a general enclosure act to deal with this wilderness. Within the next century the bare hills were laced with stone walls and large tracts of common land passed into the hands of the private speculator.

There was a great deal of enclosure in Lancashire in the later Middle Ages. The Cockersand Cartulary contains some of the earliest references to the creation of hedged fields in the Fylde. We find that at some time between 1261 and 1268 Geoffrey, son of Sir John of Hackensall, gave part of his lands at Preesall to the monks of Cockersand "with liberty to enclose, ditch, clear and plough the said land."

Although communally cultivated open fields existed around most of the villages

PLATE 15

Walney Island: an earthen field-bank faced with beach boulders and capped with turf.

in the plain (Fig. 5), it is certain that a great deal of the land in Lancashire was first cultivated in hedged and embanked fields taken in directly from the waste. A deed of 1341 tells of the clearance of one of the narrow wooded valleys that fall into the Irwell near Prestwich. It records the "grant by John de Prestwich the younger to Thurstan de Holland of a piece of land called Bradeclache in Prestwich, as inclosed by hedges and ditches in the time of its former owner, the grantor's grandfather, John, son of Adam de Prestwich, a rent of 3/4d to be paid."

The rate of enclosure quickened in the sixteenth century, and there are signs that the quiet improvement of minute patches of waste land was replaced by the fencing of acres of common and the simultaneous creation of dozens of hedged fields. Kirkham Moor was enclosed between 1554 and 1556. It lay to the west of the town and provided grazing for the burgesses of Kirkham and the inhabitants of Westby and Ribby. The new fields were allotted to the burgesses who already held land in the great open fields, the Old Earth and the Mill Field, to the south and east of Kirkham. The boundaries of the new enclosures were made of earth and later planted with quickthorns. The lease of one of these fresh enclosures from the common tells that Richard Houghton of Kirkham received "all that

FIG. 5

Litherland in 1769, showing former open field. The narrow rectangular fields to the west of the village suggest that parcels of strips in the open field have been enclosed. A few original, unenclosed strips survive immediately north of the village.

their parcell of moore grounde in Kirkeham, containing eight acres or thereabouts of late enclosed out of the common moore, by the said Richard." Here we can see the citizens of Kirkham setting about with their own hands to change the local geography and their social positions. And "Richard covenants to keep and maintain the said parcels in inclosure, making and keeping sufficiently the mounds of the same."[1]

If the general trend in the sixteenth century was towards the hedging and

[1]Shaw, *Kirkham in Amounderness*, 272.

enclosure of the commons there is one curious instance from Cartmel of the return of enclosed land to common use. The evidence lies in the will of Robert Briggs who died in 1520. He gave to Flookburgh Chapel "the farmhold occupied by John Simpson" . . . "on this condition, so that the intake which Sir William Pepper hath taken up may lie down into common again."

The results of enclosure are recorded clearly in the diaries and topographical literature of the seventeenth century. The tiny fields and high hedges had to be taken into account by the tacticians of the Civil War. Sir James Turner's diary describes a council of war conducted by the Duke of Hamilton when the Scots forces were at Hornby in the Lune valley. The question was whether they were to pass southwards through the Lancashire plain or to follow the Aire Gap and march through Yorkshire. Sir James Turner wrote, "I was for Yorkshire, and for this reason only, that I understood Lancashire was a close country, full of ditches and hedges; which was a great advantage the English would have over our raw undisciplined musketeers." Cromwell describes the scene at the battle near Preston that followed this debate as "all enclosure and miry ground" and "a lane very deep and ill" where "at last we came to a hedge dispute."

At the end of the seventeenth century Celia Fiennes leaves a picture of the landscape between Rochdale and Manchester "all enclosed with quicksets, cut smooth and as even, on fine green banks, and as well kept as for a garden, and so most of my way to Manchester I rode between such hedges; its a thing remarked by most their great curiosity in this kind."

By the early eighteenth century the last open fields of Lancashire were being enclosed. Indeed, not a single open field remained to be dealt with by the parliamentary acts and awards that were so important a factor in the shaping of the Midland landscape. In his *History of Warton*, written between 1710 and 1744, Lucas mentions that there had been five large common fields at Carnforth. He remembered the day of their enclosure and he describes the voluntary coagulation of the strips in the open fields before the confining walls were erected. At the end of the century Holt, the Board of Agriculture's surveyor, was complaining about the number of small fields in lowland Lancashire: "many hundred acres of excellent arable and pasture land are sacrificed to this stupid rage for small inclosures." When Holt made his journeys through Lancashire three types of landscape awaited the improvements that accompanied enclosure. The smooth shapes of the moors were not yet distorted by the regular grid of dark stone walls (Plate 16), the great lowland mosses had still to be criss-crossed with ditches and hedges, and the salt-marshes along the Ribble and Lune awaited their embankments, drainage channels, and large rectangular fields.

The Reclamation of the Mosses

Apart from the clearance of the natural woodland the most impressive change in the Lancashire countryside has been the transformation of the mosses into some of the best farmland in the county. Until the middle of the eighteenth century the mosslands took up a large part of the Lancashire plain. Trafford Moss and Chat Moss lay to the west of Manchester. The depression between the Billinge Ridge and the Liverpool Plateau contained Rainford and Knowsley mosses. A huge belt of mossland stretched northwards from Liverpool to the Ribble estuary and included Halsall Moss and the site of Martin Mere, described by Leland as "the biggest meare in Lancashire, three miles in length and two in breadth." The mosses were even more extensive in the Fylde. Apart from Marton Moss, which occupied the low ground inland from Blackpool, the mosses at Pilling, Rawcliffe, and Stalmine covered 20,000 acres. The immensity of this wilderness gave rise to the local saying that "Pilling Moss, like God's grace, is boundless."

PLATE 16

Gritstone walls enclose improved pastures in the Cliviger gorge on the Burnley-Todmorden road. The large rough grazings on the moor-top were enclosed about the middle of the nineteenth century.

These great wastes, a source of peat and bog oak, and the home of wild birds, were responsible for the loneliness of the Fylde and its almost complete isolation from the rest of the county. Even in the 1870's, de Rance, the geologist, collecting material for his memoir on "The superficial geology of the country adjoining the coasts of South-west Lancashire," turns away from his boulder clays to comment on the large number of idiots in the Fylde mosslands and "the dislike of the people to marry outside the district."

There are several eye-witness accounts of the reclamation of the mosses. They attracted those improving farmers who wrote books about their travels and who wished to spread the ideas of the Agricultural Revolution. In *A Six Months Tour through the North of England* Arthur Young describes the efforts of the Duke of

Bridgewater to reclaim the northern edge of Chat Moss. In the opinion of Arthur Young it was one of the finest achievements of the eighteenth century, because the reclamation of this desolate peat moss was a by-product of the new canal and labyrinth of coal mines at Worsley. "The navigation is carried a mile and a half beyond Worsley, into the middle of a large bog, called here a moss, belonging to the Duke, and merely for the use of draining it and conveying manures to improve it."

The greatest single reclamation in Lancashire was the draining of Martin Mere. As you ride into Southport on one of the expresses from Manchester it is hard to believe that the scenery of the last six miles has been made by man within the past century and a half (Plate 36). The rich dark soils, the huge rectangular fields that seem to stretch almost to the horizon, and the neat clumps of woodland, all lie on the site of what was Lancashire's largest lake. Away in the distance to the north you can see the gentle swelling of a low sandy ridge with the sites of Rufford and Holmes; this was the northern boundary of Martin Mere.

Thomas Fleetwood, the squire of Bank Hall, devised the plan for draining Martin Mere in 1692. A sluice was cut from the sea to the edge of the lake. It was one and a half miles long and passed across the salt-marsh at Crossens and through a thick deposit of peat. Previously, water had only escaped eastwards from the lake in flood time to the Douglas valley. Something of the grandeur of this piece of seventeenth-century landscape-planning can be grasped when we learn that 2,000 men were employed in cutting the new channel direct to the sea (Plate 17).

Martin Mere once again became a lake in 1755, when the flood gates that kept out the sea at high spring tides were broken through in a severe storm from the north-west that coincided with high water. It remained the home of wild birds until 1781 when Thomas Eccleston of Scarisbrick put up the capital for another attempt at reclamation. He employed Gilbert, an engineer who had worked for the Duke of Bridgewater at Worsley. A triple set of gates was built across the main sluice between the coast and the exit of the lake in 1783. In the following year several acres were put down to corn. Once again, in 1813, storms threatened the security of the new farms in the bed of Martin Mere, when the two outer gates were broken down by the sea. They were replaced by cast-iron cylinders equipped with valves, and with the help of pumping stations along the main sluice this area of rich, black soils, 10 feet below the high-water mark of spring tides, has become one of the most famous potato-growing regions in the county. Thomas Eccleston lived at a more fortunate period than the man who first conceived the idea of draining Martin Mere. This was the time when agricultural improvements, the counterpart of the revolution in industry, were fashionable among enterprising members of the squirearchy. Consequently, in 1784 he was voted the gold medal of "The Society for the Encouragement of Arts, Manufactures and Commerce."

The improvement of the North Fylde mosses started in 1830, when Wilson France of Rawcliffe Hall began to reclaim 736 acres of his estate. A dike, six miles long, was cut through Rawcliffe Moss northwards to Morecambe Bay. The whole landscape of the moss, as we see it today, was formed by this act of reclamation in the 1830's. The long straight roads were laid down to a predetermined width of seven yards and raised above the level of the moss by the peat dug from the flanking ditches. The drawing of field boundaries and drainage ditches at right-angles to the road lines completed the chessboard pattern (Fig. 6).

William Garnett, who wrote a prize essay on "Farming in Lancashire" for the Royal Agricultural Society, describes the landscape of the Pilling and Rawcliffe

PLATE 17

"The Sluice": the main drainage channel of Martin Mere was cut at the end of the seventeenth century.

mosses in the course of its transformation in 1849. "It is a dreary country in its natural state. But the hand of Man, and the blessing of Providence on his exertions, is fast converting this wilderness into a garden; oats and potatoes, turnips, and even wheat, may be seen growing in the greatest luxuriance on the surface of a bog, perhaps thirty feet deep or more, for in some parts the moss is found to exceed even this, and the black peat stacks of turf, reared to dry for fuel, may be seen standing in gloomy contrast with the smiling produce of the sickle."

The Lancashire mosses were converted into some of the best agricultural land in England in little more than a century. When Arthur Young toured the North

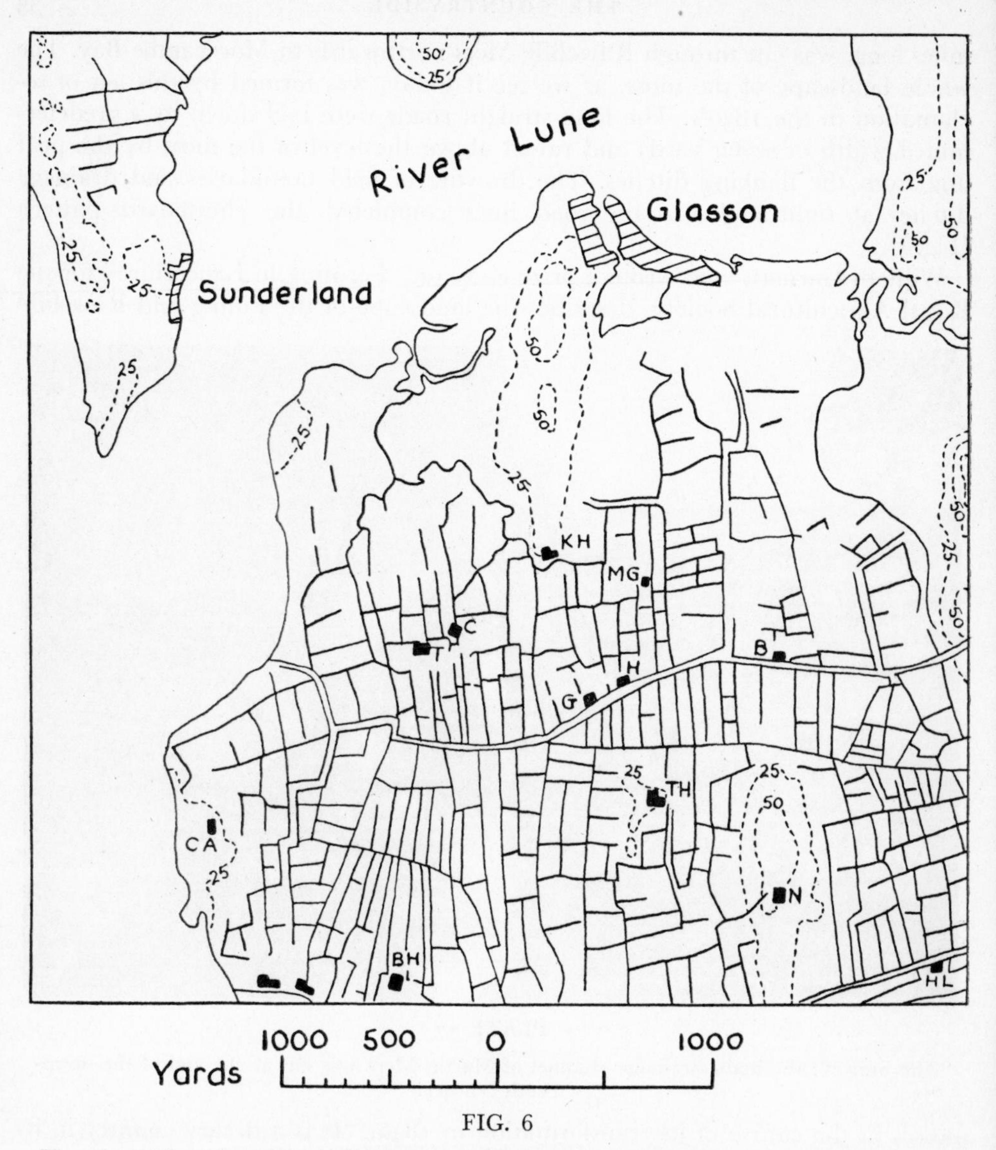

FIG. 6

Thurnham Moss: the pattern of early nineteenth-century reclamation.

Key to farm-names: KH—Kendal Hill, TH—Thursland Hill, CA—Cockersand Abbey, N—Norbrick, B—Bamber's Farm, H—Haresnape's Farm, G—Gardner's Farm, MG—Moss Grove, C—Clarkson's Farm, T—Tomlinson's Farm, BH—Bank House, HL—Hillam Lane Farm.

The old settlements with Norse place-name elements stand on the whale-backed clay hills above the 25-foot contour (*e.g.*, Thursland). The new nineteenth-century farms lie in the rectangular grid of drainage ditches, and are often named after their first owner (*e.g.*, Haresnape's Farm).

of England in 1771 the process was just beginning. By the time that de Rance was collecting the facts for the Geological Survey in the 1870's the task was almost finished. He reckoned that eighty per cent of the peat mosses were under cultivation, "except the mosses lying between Croston, Midge Hall, and Leyland, which are being gradually cut down, and the exposed surface burnt and laid down for root crops." The time of reclamation bore little relation to the difficulty of the task. Martin Mere and Chat Moss, perhaps the most formidable of these wastes, were the first to be tackled. The start of improvements depended mainly on the interests and energy of the local landowners.

Apart from the orderly and open landscapes with their network of sluices, huge

PLATE 18

A "moss cottage" at Tarlscough, Martin Mere.

fields, and scattered spinneys, the most characteristic feature of these reclaimed lands is the moss cottage (Plate 18). They are simple brick cottages, standing alone amid the wide fields, and built by speculating squires to house the labourers on the new farms. The peat provided such poor foundations that the cottages were usually erected on a base of broad flagstones imported from the Lancashire coalfield or the sandstone quarries along the Billinge ridge. With the contraction of the peat since their building many of these cottages are now standing at crazy angles.

Occasionally these labourers' cottages and small-holdings were arranged in a short terrace. You may come across a row of half a dozen houses standing among

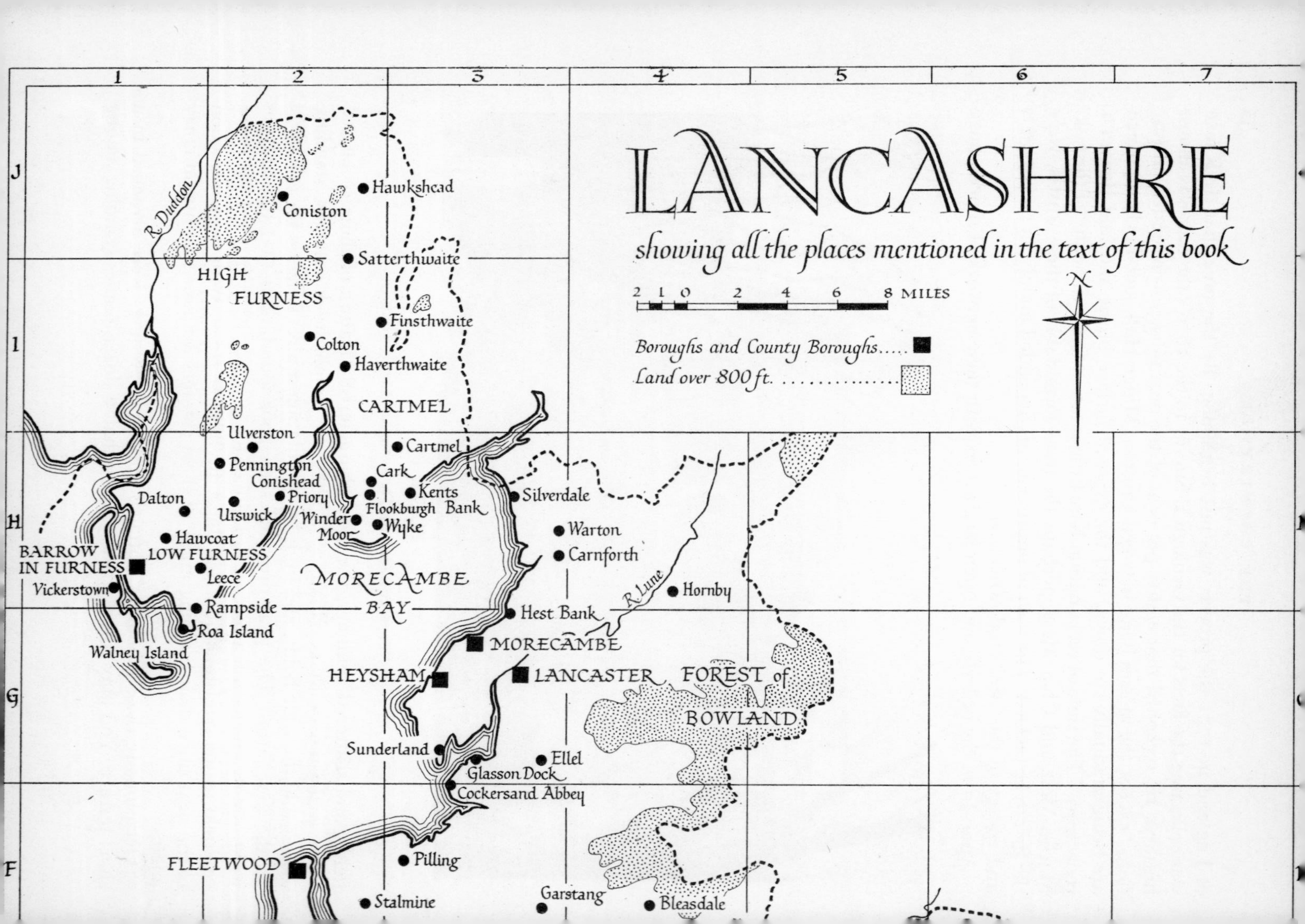
LANCASHIRE
showing all the places mentioned in the text of this book
2 1 0 2 4 6 8 MILES
Boroughs and County Boroughs.....
Land over 800 ft. ....
N
1
2
3
4
5
6
7
J
I
H
G
F
R. Duddon
Coniston
Hawkshead
Satterthwaite
HIGH
FURNESS
Finsthwaite
Colton
Haverthwaite
CARTMEL
Ulverston
Cartmel
Pennington
Conishead
Priory
Cark
Kents
Bank
Flookburgh
Dalton
Urswick
Winder
Moor
Wyke
Silverdale
Warton
Carnforth
Hawcoat
BARROW
IN FURNESS
LOW FURNESS
Leece
MORECAMBE
BAY
Vickerstown
Rampside
Roa Island
Walney Island
R. Lune
Hornby
Hest Bank
MORECAMBE
HEYSHAM
LANCASTER
FOREST of
BOWLAND
Sunderland
Ellel
Glasson Dock
Cockersand Abbey
FLEETWOOD
Pilling
Stalmine
Garstang
Bleasdale

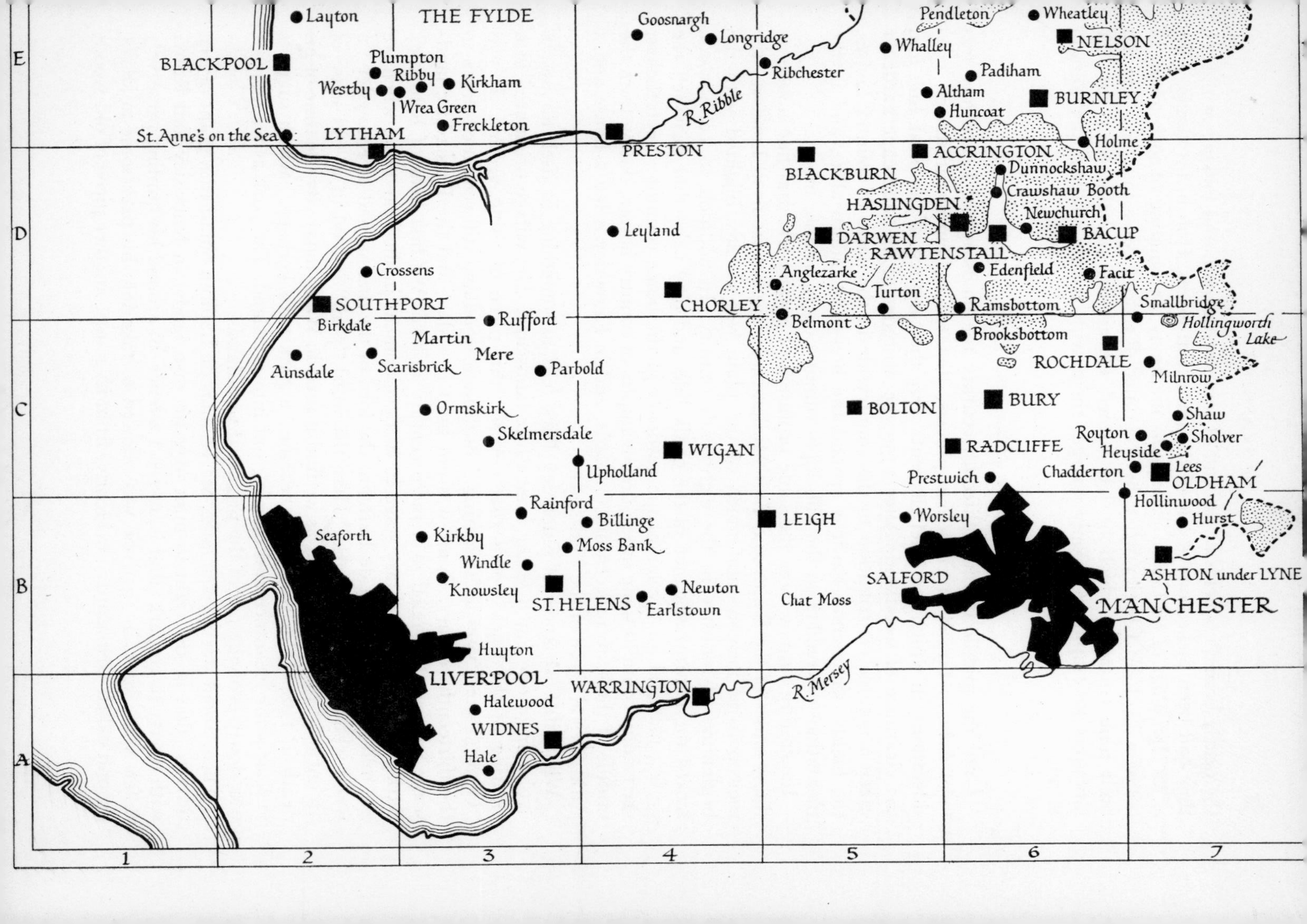
THE FYLDE
Layton
BLACKPOOL
Plumpton
Ribby
Westby
Kirkham
Wrea Green
Freckleton
St. Anne's on the Sea
LYTHAM
Goosnargh
Longridge
Ribchester
R. Ribble
PRESTON
Pendleton
Wheatley
Whalley
NELSON
Padiham
Altham
Huncoat
BURNLEY
Holme
BLACKBURN
ACCRINGTON
Dunnockshaw
Crawshaw Booth
HASLINGDEN
Newchurch
BACUP
DARWEN
RAWTENSTALL
Edenfield
Facit
Anglezarke
Turton
Ramsbottom
Smallbridge
Hollingworth Lake
Leyland
Crossens
SOUTHPORT
CHORLEY
Belmont
Brooksbottom
Birkdale
Rufford
Martin
Mere
Ainsdale
Scarisbrick
Parbold
ROCHDALE
Milnrow
Ormskirk
BOLTON
BURY
Shaw
Skelmersdale
Royton
Sholver
Heyside
WIGAN
RADCLIFFE
Upholland
Prestwich
Chadderton
Lees
OLDHAM
Rainford
Hollinwood
Billinge
LEIGH
Worsley
Hurst
Seaforth
Kirkby
Moss Bank
Windle
Knowsley
ST. HELENS
Newton
Earlstown
Chat Moss
SALFORD
ASHTON under LYNE
MANCHESTER
Huyton
LIVERPOOL
WARRINGTON
R. Mersey
Halewood
WIDNES
Hale
A
B
C
D
E
1
2
3
4
5
6
7

the nearly boundless fields at the end of some earth road, and looking as though they had been picked out of one of the industrial towns. Holt in his *General View of the Agriculture of the County of Lancaster* mentions the building of such a row of cottages by John Chorley when he reclaimed Rainford Moss in 1780. "He has built nine cottages, which he has named Cheapside, as habitations for the labourers he employs; he only charges them with twenty shillings per annum of rent."

Country Houses and Parks

Until the middle of the eighteenth century the landscape of Lancashire was formed by a largely unconscious process, dictated by purely utilitarian considerations, in which the chief elements were the conquest of the bleak hills and the clearance of woodland. After 1750 the attitudes of the landscape gardener make a notable contribution to the countryside in the parks of country houses, the highly ornamental gardens around the houses of industrialists, and in the plantations of conifers on the hill-slopes running up to heather moors.

Lancashire cannot show the same profusion of great parks and fine houses as the counties of the South and East Midlands. It was too far from London—the metropolis of fashion—and much of the plain was already blighted with the beginnings of industry in the eighteenth century. In addition its countryside lacked the natural elegance of the chalk hills and clay vales that provided the perfect material for the landscape gardener in the home counties. Nevertheless, the county contains some interesting examples of country houses, dating from the middle of the sixteenth century onwards, and in Knowsley it has a house and a park to rival those of the Midlands.

What little we know of Knowsley Park tells us something in itself about the evolution of one patch of the Lancashire landscape. The village originated in a clearing of the thick woods that covered this piece of rising ground. It was "Cenwulf's or Cynewulf's clearing." But much woodland still remained down to the thirteenth century. Rome was not built in a day; and the Lancashire landscape was not fashioned in a mere century or two. We first hear of Knowsley Park at a very rudimentary stage in its development in the year 1292, when we are told that Sir Robert de Lathom, the lord of the manor, had at Knowsley "a wood which is called a park." Here the word "park" is used in its old sense of an enclosed piece of ground, as we find it used in Wales today. By the time of his death in 1324-5 this wood had become "a park with herbage," which suggests at least some clearance and opening out into grassland. The park as we know it was slowly evolving out of the primæval woodland.

Then, about thirty years later, Sir Thomas de Lathom obtained a grant of free warren (that is, the right to hunt over his own lands) in Knowsley and Roby, with liberty to empark (that is, to erect a fence all around his hunting preserve). A few years later, in 1359, he was allowed to take into his park some adjacent ground called Grimshurst—evidently, from its name, another piece of old woodland. Clearly, the park was being enlarged during the middle years of the fourteenth century and segregated from the surrounding countryside: it was assuming more of the likeness and size of a park as we understand the word.

Until this time the park had established itself and grown at the expense of the surrounding woodland. But round about 1500 there was a significant expansion. A rental drawn up late in the reign of Henry VIII tells us that "the demesne

PLATE 19

Knowsley Park: an artificial landscape of plantations and ornamental lakes created mainly in the eighteenth century.

lands of the manor of Knowsley which were wont to be sown yearly are now enclosed within the park of Knowsley and there lie for pasture." Like so many landowners at this time, the Stanleys were enlarging their pleasure park at the expense of cornlands, and converting arable to pasture. Country houses were now being built for the pleasure of living and ostentatious display; and a large and economically useless park was considered a necessary attribute to set off a great house. Leland came this way just about this time (about 1540) and notices the park particularly—"Knollesley, a park having a pretty house of the Earls of Derby."

The more or less modest fifteenth-century house expanded with the Stanleys—in 1662 it was taxed on no fewer than seventy-two hearths, and was one of the largest houses in England—and no doubt the park grew in sympathy. By the early nineteenth century 2,000 of the 3,000 acres in the township had been brought within the park wall or the woodlands of Knowsley House, and the park extended over into the next township also. Altogether it covered some 2,500 acres and was the largest park in the North of England (Plate 19).

Astley Hall at Chorley, the home of the Charnock family, started as a timber and plaster house towards the close of the sixteenth century. During the Civil War the whole front was rebuilt in stone and brick. With its bold and abundant use of glass this is one of the most astonishing Renaissance houses in Lancashire, still more so because its park is entered directly from the main street of Chorley. The position of Astley Hall, close to the centre of Chorley, has deeply influenced the shape of the town. When expansion came in the nineteenth century, the mills and dreary terraces of industrial cottages were diverted to the empty waste of Chorley Moor on the south side of the town. Astley with its elegant park and ornamental lake remained undisturbed, a forerunner of the modern town planner's green belt.

Gawthorpe, the late Elizabethan house of the Shuttleworths, performed a similar and even more restrictive function at Padiham. Until the 1840's the landowners prevented the building of factories, and Padiham was a village of handloom weavers' cottages, in sharp contrast to the neighbouring mill town of Burnley. The marks of this phase in Padiham's history are still visible. The compact manufacturing town stands astride the River Calder, pinched in between two great parks. To the east lies Gawthorpe, its grey stone house dating from 1605 and restored in 1850 by Charles Barry, the architect of the Houses of Parliament. The park of Huntroyde climbs the slopes on the northern edge of the town to their summit in Padiham Heights. A house, rebuilt by Inigo Jones, stands concealed among its spinneys and formal drives.

Hall-i'th'-Wood, near Bolton, epitomizes several of the most important events in Lancashire's history (Plate 20). It combines the black-and-white timber work of the early sixteenth century with the cool, austere building in stone of the middle of the seventeenth century. The Brownlow family built the early part of Hall-i'th'-Wood, and the will of Lawrence Brownlow, drawn up in 1581, reveals that they were rich landowners and woollen manufacturers. Among his property he left "a water mill, two fulling mills, and other houses and lands." Hall-i'th'-Wood passed from the Brownlows to the Norris family, and in 1648 Alexander Norris added the south-west wing and porch in smooth grey sandstone. The design of the long, low windows in the wooden house is neatly matched in the stone of the later extension. Alexander Norris took the side of Parliament in the Civil War, and was treasurer to the county committee that confiscated the property of Royalists. One cannot help wondering whether the new wing at Hall-i'th'-Wood with its proud spiked finials did not grow out of some unexpected acquisition of capital from this office.

In the eighteenth century Hall-i'th'-Wood went the way of so many houses in the industrial belt of Lancashire. It was split into tenements and let to farm labourers and weavers. Among them was the father of Samuel Crompton, and in a room of this house his son invented and developed the revolutionary spinning machine, the "Hall-i'th'-Wood mule," in 1779. For most of the nineteenth century a family of tenant farmers occupied Hall-i'th'-Wood, until in 1899 it

PLATE 20

Hall-i'th'-Wood at Bolton: a striking example of the traditional black-and-white timber building of the sixteenth century.

was bought by W. H. Lever, the Bolton industrialist, and presented to the town as a historic monument. Hall-i'th'-Wood, almost enveloped by Bolton's bleach works and spinning mills, has become a museum of the cotton industry and a memorial to the technical genius of Samuel Crompton.

Lancashire contains no eighteenth-century houses to match the fine buildings of that period in the South of England. Sir Thomas Egerton commissioned James Wyatt to design one of the best mansions of this period in 1772 (Plate 21). This low, classical building stands in a great park that takes up most of the old township of Heaton. In 1901 Manchester Corporation bought Heaton House and opened the grounds as a public park, providing a valuable open space on the edge of Cheetham Hill and Crumpsall, two of the most closely built suburbs of the city. A "temple" stands a few yards from the house on the tip of a spur that falls away to the Irk valley. Baines in his *History of the County Palatine and Duchy of Lancaster* (1836) describes the scene from this folly as "commanding extensive views in the four adjoining counties of Cheshire, Derbyshire, Staffordshire and Yorkshire." Today, when one stands on the open space in front of Wyatt's neat little temple the panorama that unfolds to the south tells the whole story of the end of Heaton House as a wealthy residence. Above the round, umber-coloured bluffs of the Irk runs an artificial skyline of roofs, whole streets in length, and

PLATE 21

Heaton House at Manchester as it was about 1830. It was designed by James Wyatt in 1772 for Sir Thomas Egerton, and is now owned by Manchester Corporation.

factory chimneys belching smoke as foul as the grey-blue waste of the bleach works that poisons the stream in the valley floor.

Lancashire's manufacturers built a large number of mansions in the nineteenth century. In the east and south, within the area of the industrial towns, they all look very much alike. A small and ornamental garden usually lies behind a heavy screen of trees. Amid the towering rhododendrons and rockeries built of local sandstone and garnished with plants from the high Alps stands a grim square house, its vacant, uninviting windows set in Victorian sashes and the heavy blocks of square-cut sandstone covered with a grey slime of soot from the nearby mills. These houses, which can be seen again and again in the respectable suburbs of Rochdale, Oldham, and Bury, express so clearly the ideals and outlooks of Lancashire's Victorian cotton spinners and textile merchants. Just as the pleasant pastures of the Fylde, the tidy tree-lined hedgerows, and the airy parks were part of the way of life of her small squires, so the mountains of rhododendron and the dark houses lost among rain-dripping trees seem to spring from the card-room, the chapel, and the counting-house.

There are some notable examples of the Gothic Revival among the country houses of Lancashire. Conishead Priory, Ulverston, is an ideal illustration of this bizarre aspect of the Romantic Movement. Its site, on ground that had been occupied by the ruins of the priory, provided a very proper setting for a piece of Gothic Revival. The building started in 1821 and took fifteen years to complete, with a huge baronial hall and two "minaret towers" over 100 feet high. The park contained "a new American flower garden" and a conservatory that specialized in the breeding of hybrid rhododendrons, one of which was called the Rhododendron Ulverstoniana. A chapel and a newly constructed "ruined castle," "The Hermitage," crowned a low hill to the north of the Priory. This tremendous effort to combine the comforts of industrial England with medieval romance ruined the Bradyll family. In 1850 Colonel Bradyll was forced to sell his grandiose house. Later it became a hydro, and *Murray's Handbook* said in 1880 that "a lovelier place for invalids could not be found." Today Conishead is a rest home for miners from the Durham coalfield and this great house, designed by Philip Wyatt in the spirit of the Romantic Movement, still impresses by its magnificence.

The building of great houses and the designing of parks, the most deliberately conceived types of landscape, came to an end with the close of the nineteenth century. The present use of most of these houses shows that our society has reached a state in which their proper purpose, as private homes, has become impossible. The evolution of the country house into the public institution has been driven further in Lancashire than in the South Midlands by the growth of industries and the destruction of the countryside. Tastes change; the wealthy manufacturer has long ceased to live within sight of his works. He lives at Blackpool and Southport or in the resorts of North Wales and makes the daily journey to Manchester by the "club train." Edwin Butterworth noted the start of this process, even though he did not foresee the daily journey to work, when he gathered material for his *Historical Sketches of Oldham* in the 1840's. He reports that Joseph Jones, a master cotton spinner and at that time one of the chief landowners in Oldham, left Wallshaw House to live in a Worcestershire village. At a later date, John Platt, manufacturer of textile machinery, promoter of technical education in Oldham, and a heavy investor in the railways of East Lancashire, claimed to be responsible for the development of Llanfairfechan as a resort. As one looks at the country houses of Lancashire today it is hard to believe that Sir John Gerard entertained the future emperor, Napoleon III, at Garswood in 1846; and that they had a hunting expedition in Windle, a township now cut in two by the East Lancashire Road and buried beneath the brick suburbs of St. Helens.

Plantations

Although natural woodland formed one of the chief obstacles to the early settlement of Lancashire, the tree-studded hedgerows and the neat rectangular spinneys of the modern landscape are largely a result of planting over the last two centuries. Several of the pleasant woods along the road from Burnley to Todmorden were first planted at the close of the eighteenth century, when Dr. Whitaker, the historian of Manchester, put more than a million seedlings into his estate at Holme. Baines, in his *Lancashire Directory* (1825), describes how "the bare and rocky brows, the glens and gullies upon the estate of Holme were filled with forest trees."

High Furness is now the most wooded part of Lancashire. In no sense is this landscape of dense low-growing oak and birch wood a primitive forest. Two centuries of careful cultivation with repeated cuttings at intervals of fifteen to twenty-five years have produced the thick stands of copsewood. Cowper, the local historian of Hawkshead, believed that tall timber trees disappeared from High Furness in the latter half of the seventeenth century. In a survey of the Lordship of Furness in 1649 the commissioners estimated the timber resources of the district. "There are growing upon the lands of the customary tenants in High Furness between three and four thousand timber trees." Cowper claims that most of these tall trees disappeared in the wave of rebuilding after 1650. Today the relics of this forest can be seen in the massive bread chests and the roof-trees of farms and barns among the hills of Furness.

The rising demand for charcoal in the new iron forges of the eighteenth century and the depletion of the forests of Furness turned timber into a valuable commodity, one that could be cultivated and preserved. From this time, and out of the insatiable appetite of the forges for one oak tree per week, we can date the neat coppices that clothe the slopes of the fells between Coniston and Windermere. The dense coppice woodland sprang from the roots of the felled trees, and Hodgson in his *Topographical Description of Westmorland* (1820) claims that it was worth £10 and £15 an acre and "as much as £20, if composed entirely of oaks."

The value of coppice rose to such heights towards the close of the eighteenth century that woods were enclosed and moors planted with trees. The establishment of bobbin mills at Force Forge and Stot Park led to the planting of coppice in Satterthwaite and Colton. Between 1782 and 1785 the hillsides above Grizedale were clothed with fresh woods. In 1782 Miss Ford planted 5,300 oaks on her Grizedale estate. Two years later she extended her coppice wood with 12,000 ash and 46,000 oak trees. As one walks along the pleasant lane by Grizedale Beck from Satterthwaite to Hawkshead it is hard to believe that these windswept, hummocky woods were put there by design. But the names of these plantations bring back long-lost associations from the days when the seedlings first went into the ground. The larch woods with which the Ainslie family covered Grizedale

Moor recall their connections with the Far East in names like Guinea Hill, New South Wales, and China.

As we travel through Lancashire today it is difficult to point to a landscape undisturbed by man. When the Romans came to Britain woods covered the Lancashire hills up to heights of more than a thousand feet. The bare horizons of the Forest of Bowland, that under a slow procession of cumulus clouds create the same sense of space as the open sea, are themselves a product of history. In the course of a thousand years men have burnt, cut, and grubbed up the forests. Even the associations of grasses that succeeded the trees have been severely modified by man and his grazing animals. Perhaps only in the fragments of salt-marsh on Morecambe Bay and at the mouth of the Ribble, drowned by every high spring tide, do we see a landscape unchanged by man. Even these wastes between land and sea lie open to the prospect of some imaginative piece of engineering that at one stroke would reclaim the area of several parishes. If George Stephenson had had his way in 1837 he would have constructed a seven-mile-long railway embankment from Hest Bank to Humphrey Head, changing the whole geography of the inner part of Morecambe Bay.

III

The Urban Landscape

THE majority of Lancashire's towns are a by-product of the Industrial Revolution, and at first sight they look monotonously alike with their drab streets, towering mills, and soot-stained chapels. Yet a search through the scores of local histories written in the last century will show that each town has its rich and interesting story, one which often differs fundamentally from the history of its closest neighbour.

Two hundred years ago Rochdale was a busy market town, while Oldham was still a tiny hamlet set amid the threadbare living of scattered farms on the edge of the Pennine moors. Even today, when Rochdale and Oldham each house more than a hundred thousand people, the heart of the former has the air of a market centre, and the latter looks as though it had been built only to serve the needs of its cotton mills. Again, the textile towns in the deep furrows among the Rossendale hills have a different plan and style of architecture from the glass and chemical towns in the south-west of the county. At Bacup the solid grey stone was hewn from the local hillsides to build the rows of terraced houses that fence the steep cobbled streets. The old textile towns seem to have no plan; tiny, two-storied mills, dwelling-houses, and nonconformist chapels are jumbled together without any suggestion of order. By contrast, St. Helens and Widnes spread in a rash of glazed red brick across the fertile plain of South-west Lancashire in the second half of the nineteenth century. There is scarcely a factory in their residential districts and outwardly they look like Rugby, Nuneaton, or Leicester, the Victorian red-brick towns of the Midlands. Their glass and chemical works are concentrated on sites of enormous area, littered with chimneys and the surrealistic devices of complicated heavy industries and fantastic mountains of slag on which a few blades of grey grass struggle for life. These two types of industrial town are completely different from each other in their development and shape.

Not all the towns are the product of our Victorian forefathers and their manufactures. Ulverston was the capital of the remote Furness peninsula until it was supplanted by Barrow in the second half of the nineteenth century. Its solid banks and fine Georgian houses remind us of a time when Ulverston was the commercial focus and fashionable winter residence for all the district from the head of Windermere to the bleak salt-marshes on Walney Island. Preston, at first sight nothing but a Victorian cotton town, stands at the head of the Amounderness Hundred in Domesday Book and was granted a borough charter in 1179. During the eighteenth century it contained many town houses of the country gentry, and Dr. Whitaker described it as "an elegant and economical town, the resort of well born but ill-portioned and ill-endowed old maids and widows." In 1777, when Messrs. Collinson and Watson built their first spinning mill, Preston started its career as an industrial town and slowly ceased to be a fashionable resort (Plate 22).

When did towns first make their appearance in the Lancashire landscape? We can be sure that there were none before the Romans occupied the north of England and came to build their roads and forts. Important towns like Lancaster, Manchester, and Wigan are built over the rectangular embanked enclosures that were Roman forts, but there is no evidence that urban ways of life have continuously existed there.

Six Roman roads converge on Manchester. Even in that distant period it was

PLATE 22

Preston: the market-place about 1830. At this date Preston still had the atmosphere of a country town. Sir Gilbert Scott's town hall (1867) now fills the space occupied by the Georgian town hall and timbered shops in the background.

one of the most important places in Lancashire. The site of the Roman station now lies in one of the most dismal parts of the city, caught up in an area of slum property where the tangled railway tracks stride out of the Central station on a huge viaduct. There is a detailed description of this Roman site, Castlefield, as Dr. Whitaker found it in the 1760's when he was writing his *History of Manchester*. He describes a landscape of cottages and gardens on a bluff above the Irwell, where "the remaining parts of the wall rise five, six, and four feet in height, lined all the way with a thick uninterrupted hedge of thorns above, and exhibiting a broken chequered scenery to the eye below." Today, amid the stench of diesel oil, we are still reminded of that pleasant haunt of eighteenth-century antiquarians by the name of Castle Street that leads to the site of Castlefield.

Manchester grew into a small town after the Norman Conquest. It stood on a gentle bluff above the River Irwell a mile to the east of the Roman fort. The new centre was the church that became Manchester Cathedral in the nineteenth century. An inscribed stone, found in excavations at the Cathedral in 1871, suggests that a church was standing there in pre-Norman times. Though this slender evidence points to the use of the site of Manchester before the Norman Conquest, the appearance of town life can best be dated back to the early Middle Ages.

The Creation of Boroughs

The Norman Conquest brought England into closer contact with the rest of Europe at a time when long-distance trade was increasing and towns were being founded in great numbers beneath the walls of castles, at the gates of abbeys, and at the natural points where traffic converged. Lancashire shared in this general rise of prosperity in the twelfth and thirteenth centuries. No fewer than twenty-three boroughs were created in the county between 1066 and 1372, but most of them proved to be failures as towns. At the end of the Middle Ages only four of these boroughs—Lancaster, Preston, Wigan, and Liverpool—were still regarded as such. The loss of urban rights by almost a score of Lancashire towns, including Manchester, provides a melancholy reminder that History is not a story of continuous success.

The granting of a borough charter recognized the main economic functions of a town, trade and industry, and released its inhabitants from most of the services borne by countrymen in feudal society. The Preston charter of 1252, confirming the original charter of 1179, gives a vivid picture of the expansion of the town about this time. It speaks of the need for more land, and gives the burgesses of Preston the right to cultivate a strip of heath on the edge of the royal forest of Fulwood that stretched away into the hills of Bowland from the northern edge of the town: "they may break up and reduce to cultivation the moor towards our wood of Fulwood . . . as they shall please without hindrance from our foresters and verderers." Another paragraph of the charter instructs the burgesses of Preston to divide their new arable land from the royal hunting grounds with fencing taken from the forest. Today a fashionable residential suburb of widely spaced Victorian houses stands on this piece of land that was brought in from the royal forest by the expanding town of Preston in the middle of the thirteenth century.

When Preston, Lancaster, Wigan, and Manchester received their borough charters it is probable that settlements with small industries and some local trade were already in existence. At Liverpool the words of the first charter, granted by King John in 1207, paint a picture of a town that is about to be made. "John . . . to all his lieges who wish to have burgages at the town of Liverpool, greeting. . . . And so we order you that securely and in our peace you come thither to receive and inhabit your burgages." Here is a clear invitation for settlers to come and help in the creation of a new port on the Mersey estuary "with all the liberties and free customs . . . which any free borough on the sea has in our land." Not until twenty-five years later did William Ferrers, Earl of Derby, build his castle at Liverpool. In most places the growth of towns proceeded in the opposite way: streets of houses gathered beneath the ramparts of a fortress, markets were held, and finally the functions and privileges of a town were confirmed in a borough charter.

Warrington, an important town on the Mersey, shows the political misfortunes that could overtake a borough. William le Botiller, lord of the manor, granted a charter to the town in 1292. Eight years later another document shows that the burgesses were forced to give up their borough court and to take their disputes once again to the manorial court of the Botillers. Here is an instance, not uncommon in Lancashire, of the restriction of the growth of a town by the envy and power of a manorial lord.

Several places in Furness illustrate the fitful prosperity of towns that received their borough charters in the thirteenth century. Before the Norman Conquest Dalton stood at the head of the manors of Plain Furness. After the greater part of the peninsula had been given to the Cistercian monks who founded Furness Abbey in 1127 Dalton emerged as an important town, a regional capital for Furness. Today there remains no evidence of Dalton's borough status apart from a few references to burgages in medieval documents. For instance, in 1276 Thomas Skilehar, burgess of Dalton, gave the monks of Furness Abbey permission to take 100 waggon loads of turf from his moss at Angerton. The exact date of Dalton's first charter is not known, but the establishment of a fair in 1239 undoubtedly gives some close indication of the date. This little town failed to maintain its position as a borough and in the great clearing-up of local government at the end of the nineteenth century was placed under an urban district council.

Roger de Lancaster granted a charter to Ulverston in 1284 and created a small borough with thirty burgesses. Although this attractive grey town took Dalton's place as the regional capital of Furness after the dissolution of the monasteries it, too, failed to retain its borough status. Since 1894 Ulverston has been ruled by an urban district council.

Several other places in North Lancashire received borough charters in the thirteenth century and today look even less like towns than Ulverston and Dalton. Warton, at the head of Morecambe Bay, where the austere limestone hills come down to the sands, was granted a charter by Walter de Lindsay some time between 1246 and 1271. He gave it all the customs of Kendal and Ulverston. The trades of dyers and fullers were to be protected, and there were arrangements for the use of the common fields to the east and west of the town. Warton never assumed the outward shape of a town, despite its fame for shipbuilding in the eighteenth century. When Lucas wrote his fascinating and detailed parish history between 1710 and 1744 it was still a village of farmers. Today, the fifteenth-century church stands in the middle of a long street whose plan has scarcely changed since the Middle Ages. The fine medieval rectory has long been a ruin.

Archbishop Hutton's grammar school, founded in 1594, had been converted into cottages when Lucas was writing his impressions.

Flookburgh is a straggling village of grey rough-cast cottages on the old road across the Cartmel peninsula between the Kent and Leven sands. It received a borough charter in the early Middle Ages, but all evidence of the exact date of the document has disappeared. Flookburgh's lost history as a town is first revealed in a deed of 1610, when James I gave "George Salter and others sixty-five burgages and sixty-five tofts in Flookburgh, part of the priory of Cartmel." Flookburgh, like Dalton, probably owed its charter to a community of monks, the Augustinian priory at Cartmel. Flookburgh's sixty-five burgages show that it was more than twice the size of Ulverston. Its failure to develop into a town can hardly be attributed to blind geographical fate, because the settlement stands on the most direct road across the Cartmel peninsula, the main entry into Furness until the railway was thrown across the wide estuaries of the Kent and Leven in 1857. Flookburgh was strangled by the growth of Cartmel as a market centre and stopping-place for the convoys of travellers on the wild track across the sands between Furness and Lancaster. The details of the decline of Flookburgh are probably beyond recovery. No doubt some whim of a prior of Cartmel transferred the trade of the peninsula to the little settlement at the priory gate, and from that time Flookburgh, with all the advantages of its site, fell from the high promise that was expressed by its borough charter.

At the end of the fifteenth century only four of Lancashire's towns retained the full privileges and government of a chartered borough. They were Wigan, Preston, Lancaster, and Liverpool. The last mentioned was already the chief port of the county and the others all stood on the great road to the north.

The Legacy of the Middle Ages

In the old towns of Lancashire medieval building has been almost completely swept away by the industrial architecture of the last century. Warrington could hardly be called an architectural treasure house. Apart from a few streets of pleasant Georgian buildings in a warm red brick and a black-and-white timbered public-house of 1661, the town was almost completely rebuilt in the nineteenth century. Yet the street pattern of the town centre has been inherited from a much earlier period. The first feature of Warrington's plan to attract attention is the position of the parish church, situated a quarter of a mile to the east of the market place—the present focus of the town. This is explained by the fact that the earliest entry into Warrington from the south was by a shallow ford across the Mersey that came in at the site of the parish church. About the end of the thirteenth century a new bridge was built a quarter of a mile down the river from the old crossing. It is first mentioned in a document of 1304, when "Sir William le Botiller, Lord of Warrington, granted to Jordan fitz Robert de Sonke a plot of land near the Bridge of Merse." In 1364 Edward III authorized the rebuilding of the Mersey Bridge. From the fourteenth century onward this bridge formed the main entrance into the town from the south, and with its construction the road to the north and the centre of Warrington were shifted to the west of the original focus at the parish church. At the same time a new street, called Newgate, was built northwards into the town. This important river-crossing, the main route into Lancashire, was again improved in 1495, when the Earl of Derby built a new bridge in honour of Henry VII's journey to Lathom House. At this time the main street of Warrington changed its name from Newgate to Bridge Street, a name it has borne ever since.

Preston today is a museum of Victorian architecture and its street plan at the centre is the only memorial of the medieval town. The east-west line of Fishergate and Church Street probably lies on the site of the long street of an Anglian village founded some time in the seventh century. The junction of the Friargate at the town centre was the cross-road of the short north-south street that led out into the common fields on the open fertile bluff above the Ribble. Centuries of town life have almost destroyed this first plan of Preston, but out in the soft green countryside of the Fylde, villages like Kirkham and Freckleton preserve this primitive design of two streets at right-angles to each other.

Even if the buildings of medieval Lancashire have largely disappeared, many of the anomalies in the political geography of the county owe their origin to that time. Lancaster is still the county town, although it lies remote from the great centres of population around Liverpool and Manchester. This fact of modern geography was settled in the years immediately after the Norman Conquest, when Count Roger of Poitou received his reward of estates in Lancashire. He chose a low hill, looking like an upturned boat, on the south bank of the Lune as the site for his great castle. Domesday Book shows that Lancaster was insignificant at this time; in fact, there is no separate entry for the town and it is reckoned as part of the manor of Halton, now a quiet village on the Lune two miles away.

Roger's castle was superbly placed to survey the northern marches of his territory, and from these beginnings the town that grew at its feet became the administrative centre of the County Palatine. Geographically, Roger of Poitou could have improved upon his site for the county town. Preston, on the same road to the north and more centrally placed between the Fylde and the South Lancashire plain, was a logical choice for the political capital. The wonder is that Preston did not take over this position at some time in history. For a short period in the thirteenth century the Assize Courts were transferred to Preston from Lancaster; the Courts of the Duchy of Lancaster were held there from 1351 to 1361; in the seventeenth century the establishment of the Chancery Court of the Duchy turned it into a lawyers' town. Today much of the government of Lancashire is centred in Preston, though Lancaster still retains the title and some of the functions that arose out of Roger of Poitou's organization of his estates.

Another legacy of the distribution of the spoils of the Norman Conquest is the division of Manchester into two cities: Salford and Manchester. They were part of one manor before Roger of Poitou gave the lands to the south of the Irwell to his vassal, Albert Grelley. Eight centuries have failed to obliterate this division between the manors of Manchester and Salford. Count Roger's gift explains many of the inconveniences of travelling from one side of the city to the other at the present time, when one has to walk in the grey drizzling rain between the 'bus termini of the Manchester and Salford Corporations.

The Rise of Industrial Towns

The Middle Ages have left no great monuments in the towns of Lancashire. The county stood in economic isolation; the main streams of industry and trade flowed elsewhere, through the streets of the great commercial cities in the south of England. In the years about 1780 the Industrial Revolution started to change the Lancashire landscape. The discovery of steam power, the invention of machines that had to be installed in mills instead of the high garrets of upland farms, and a widening market for cotton textiles, caused the growth of spinning towns in the South Lancashire plain. Some industrial towns, like Preston and Bolton, grew out of long-established market centres, others arose rapidly amidst farms and fields hitherto innocent of houses (Fig. 7).

Oldham was transformed into a town within the last quarter of the eighteenth century. It developed around a cross-roads on the southern slopes of Oldham Edge, a sharp sandstone ridge in the Coal Measures facing eastward to the bare wall of the Pennines. A map of the township of Oldham in 1756 shows the parish church and a handful of scattered hamlets with pleasant country names like Roundthorn, Smithy Fold, and Priesthill, all set amidst acres of unimproved moor. Within fifty years the pastures of Oldham Edge were rapidly overgrown with lines of unpaved streets; the severe gritstone farmhouses were swamped by small two- and three-storey mills, rows of cottages, and the brick-built mansions of the new industrialists. Edwin Butterworth in his *Historical Sketches of Oldham* (1849) sums up this period between 1770 and 1810, when England's greatest cotton-spinning town appeared on the map: "the place underwent an extraordinary change from the scale of a mere village to that of one of the most populous towns in the kingdom."

The period of most rapid growth in the textile towns was between 1780 and 1840. Towards the middle of the nineteenth century new types of industry appeared in Lancashire and gave rise to new towns. After 1850 St. Helens enlarged at an astonishing rate with the growth of the glass and chemical industries. Widnes only started in 1847, when the alkali industry was established on the flat shore at the head of the Mersey estuary.

Barrow-in-Furness is a still more striking product of the Victorian period (Fig. 8). In 1840 Barrow was no more than a collection of cottages on the edge of the sheltered channel that separates Walney Island from the mainland. A few crude wooden jetties projected into this fine natural harbour and they were used for loading the red iron ore brought by hired farm carts from the mines of Plain Furness. Barrow was brought into being by the building of the first length of the

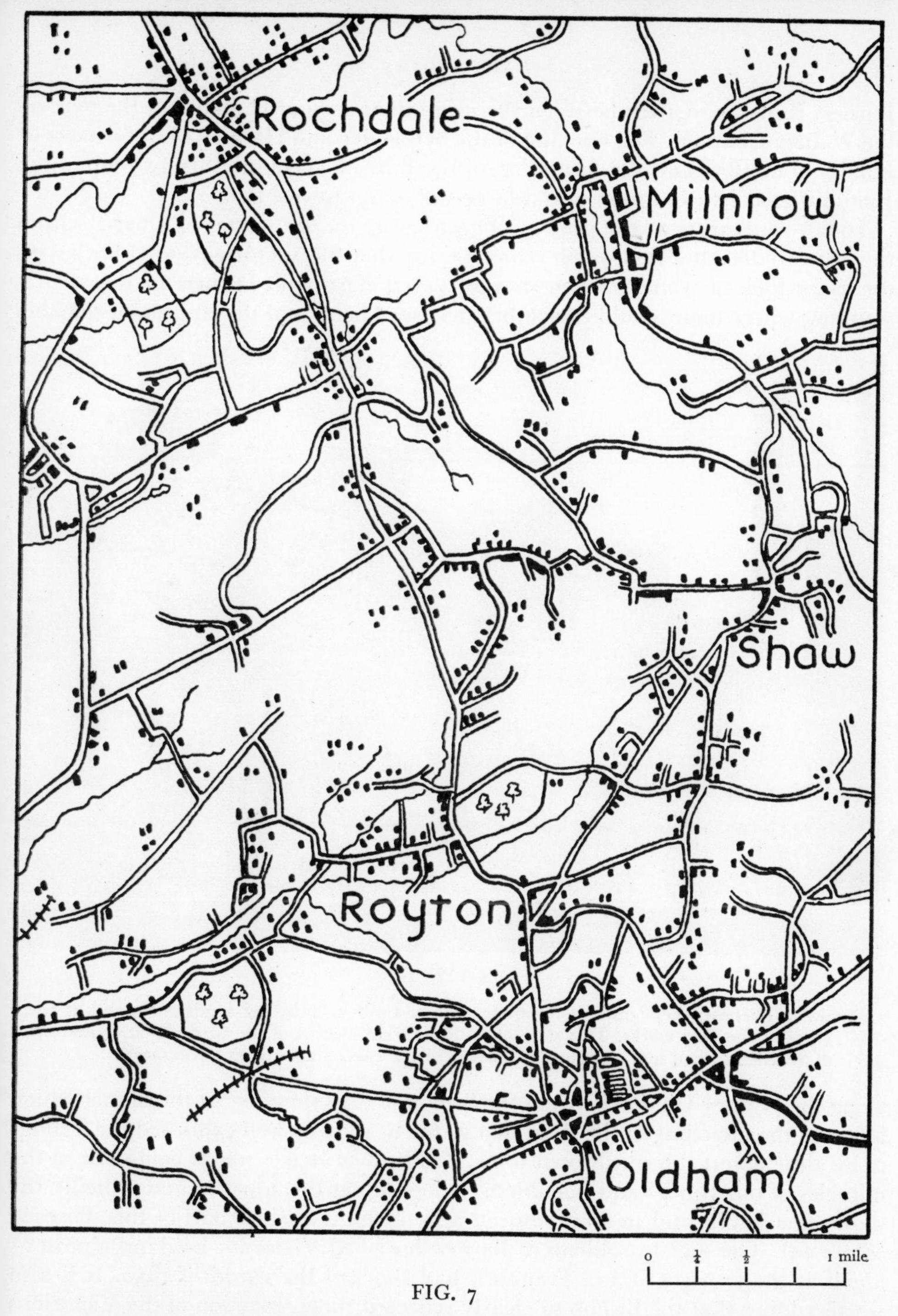

FIG. 7

Early industrial landscape between Oldham and Rochdale: from Teesdale's Map (1828-9). This shows the settlement pattern of South-east Lancashire before the growth of the great industrial towns, with small farms, engaged in cloth-manufacturing as a by-employment, scattered along the lanes.

Furness Railway in 1846 between the iron mines around Dalton and the port on the Walney Channel. The opening of the Schneider and Hannay blast furnaces at Hindpool in 1859 and the formation of the Barrow Hæmatite Steel Company in 1866 initiated its expansion into a large industrial town.

Today we marvel at the growth of great cities on the wastes of Siberia within the last two decades. It is worth remembering that the Victorians stood back with the same look of wonder when they surveyed Barrow-in-Furness in the 1870's, standing where many could remember the green fields and the empty salt-marshes

PLATE 23

Barrow-in-Furness: these mid-Victorian tenements built of local red sandstone stand at the gates of the iron works. This style of building, reminiscent of the working-class quarters of Scottish towns, was common in Barrow in the early stages of its development.

along the Walney Channel. When the Bishop of Carlisle spoke at the dinner which followed the unveiling of the Ramsden statue in 1872 he well expressed the feelings of his time about this mushroom town. "This town strikes me as being one of the miracles of our time," and he added, "I look upon this town as undoubtedly the most remarkable, and in some respects also the most anxious part of this diocese" (Plate 23). The social problems of Barrow horrified Victorian England almost as much as the excesses of San Francisco had shocked the world of 1850. It is also worth adding that the Bishop so clearly reflected the satisfaction of the Victorians when they contemplated their world-wide trade, their factories, their Gothic churches and ornate town halls: "I rejoice that my lot has been cast in a century so full of wonder, and I think, also, so full of hope."

Barrow's period of most rapid growth and highest hopes lay in the decade 1871-81, when her population increased from under 20,000 to nearly 50,000. But this epoch of explosive expansion was very brief. The census returns for 1891 reveal a loss by migration of nearly 6,000 people, a movement that is concealed in the total figures for the borough at that time by the high birth rate and rapid natural increase of the population.

Barrow's instability is largely explained by its unfortunate industrial history. Today it relies almost entirely on shipbuilding and heavy engineering; for the rest it is a story of dismal failures over the past seventy years. The most spectacular was the collapse of the Barrow and Calcutta Jute Company. F. Leach, a contemporary journalist, described the jute mill "designed in red brick and terra cotta in a style of architecture adapted from the Italian" as "one of the largest and finest manufacturing works in the kingdom." It was founded in 1870 by Sir James Ramsden, director of the Furness Railway and of the Barrow Iron Shipbuilding Company, six times mayor of the borough, and more than anyone else the creator of this industrial town. Ramsden introduced the jute industry as a counterbalance to the heavy industries of Barrow. At its peak the mill found work for more than 2,000 women, and ships sailed directly from Calcutta to Barrow with the raw material. After a fire that destroyed more than half the factory in 1892 the jute industry collapsed and Barrow ceased to be a rival to Dundee. There is a long list of other industries that failed or were closed down through the "rationalizing processes" of large organizations. The plant of the Barrow Salt Company at the south end of Walney Island was bought by the great Cheshire salt combine and closed down in 1909; the locomotive and carriage works and repair shops of the Furness Railway went out of existence when the L.M.S. absorbed the line in 1923. Several small engineering works and iron foundries have disappeared and the claypits and kilns that supplied the bricks for the building of Barrow have long been abandoned. The silent dock basins and disused piers tell the same melancholy story of the frustration of the high ambition of the 1870's. James Ramsden planned to make Barrow one of the leading ports of the north-west. Its failure is the story of a hopeless struggle against Liverpool, Preston, Fleetwood, and Heysham. At the end of the remote Furness peninsula, Barrow is badly placed to serve the great centres of population and industry in South Lancashire and the West Riding, while the Furness Railway Company's attempts to develop passenger services with Belfast, Dublin, and the Isle of Man were finally broken by the rivalry of Heysham and Fleetwood and the railway amalgamation of 1923.

Ramsbottom epitomizes the history of the small manufacturing town (Plate 24). Its grey sandstone mills and long rows of stone cottages fill the narrow Irwell valley a few miles above Bury. At the end of the eighteenth century there were only a few cottages on the site of Ramsbottom. It was then part of Holcombe, a

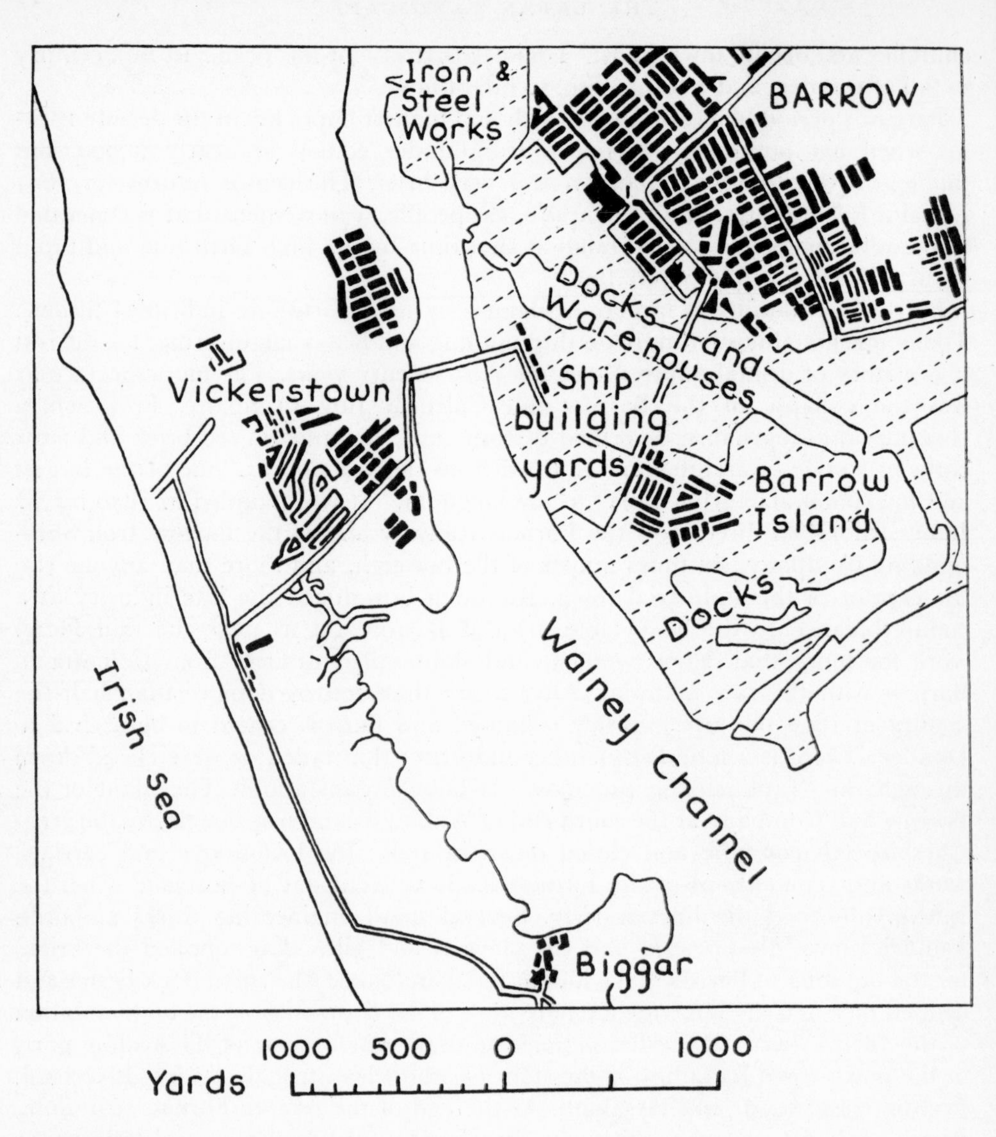

FIG. 8

Barrow-in-Furness: a Victorian town with a grid-iron plan. Barrow started to grow in 1846 on the Duke of Devonshire's land. Barrow Old Island became an industrial quarter in the 1870's and at the turn of the century Vickerstown was founded as a "marine garden city." Biggar, a tight knot of farms, retains the plan of a Norse hamlet.

small hamlet in a district of isolated farms that had formed a chapelry in the large parish of Bury since the late Middle Ages.

Factories first appeared in the Irwell valley when Robert Peel established the "Ground Calico Printing Works" at Bury in 1770. The firm of Peel, Yates, and Tipping became so prosperous that they rapidly established subsidiary printing mills and extended into allied branches of the industry, setting up cotton mills to spin and weave the material for printing and a chemical works at Radcliffe to supply the bleaching powders. As part of this expansion Peel built the first mill, a print works, at Ramsbottom in 1780.

PLATE 24

Ramsbottom: a nineteenth-century industrial town in the Irwell valley that grew under the wing of the Grant brothers. The Peel Tower on the skyline of Holcombe Hill was put up in 1852 to commemorate the repeal of the Corn Laws.

Although Robert Peel was the founder of industry in Ramsbottom, the growth of the town depended upon the fortunes of the Grant family. Two brothers, William and Daniel Grant, partners in a drapers' shop in Bury, bought the print works in 1805. A little later they built a cotton mill at Ramsbottom, and as Barton, one of the historians of Bury, writes, "then commenced their fabulous rate of money making—buying the cotton in the raw state, selling it printed, dyed and finished, or bartering with foreign merchants; thus securing to themselves all the profits of these well-paying trades."

Today Ramsbottom is full of the memorials of this success story. There is the chain of mills along the Irwell, and the dour streets of gritstone cottages, many of which were built for the workers who were brought from as far away as Hull and London. When they became rich the Grants flaunted their wealth in the curious "Scots Baronial" style of St. Andrew's Church and the gloomy house, Nuttall Hall, which they placed in the valley floor under the shadow of their cotton mills. On a hillside above the grey roofs and chimney stacks of Ramsbottom William Grant erected Grant's Tower, a fantastic Gothic folly that was intended to commemorate his father's journey to Lancashire in 1783 in search of work. Some of the memorials of Ramsbottom's early industrial history have already disappeared. Grant's Tower was brought down by a great gale that swept across Lancashire in the spring of 1943. The derelict Nuttall Hall was dismantled by the Ramsbottom Council in 1952. Its sombre ornate garden, shut in by mountainous rhododendrons and dripping trees, is preserved as a public park.

The picturesque story of the Grants was held up as an example to Victorian England of what could be achieved by initiative and hard work. Samuel Smiles used them as a model in *Self Help*, and they reappear in the pages of Dickens as the Cheeryble brothers. In the history of Lancashire they stand as an example of one of the many families who put a new town on the map. Until the 1860's the direction of the life of Ramsbottom was largely in the hands of the Grant family. Master and workers lived close together. From the gardens of Nuttall House you can see the chimneys and sheds of the bleach works and cotton mills. Its west windows look out to the battlemented turrets of St. Andrew's Church, and the whole settlement is shut in by the austere skylines of the Rossendale moors. In his *History of Bury* Barton claims that Ramsbottom formed a stable community of masters and workers, free from the violent discontent of the big towns like Rochdale and Oldham. He cites the fact that apprenticeships ran in families for several generations, but one should also remember that this little town was a stronghold of Radicals and the Chartist Movement—perhaps a natural reaction in a closed community where the master family had built the mills, several of the streets of houses, and the chapel.

A mile below Ramsbottom, where the Irwell cuts through a hard band of sandstone in a pleasant wooded gorge, the history of Ramsbottom is repeated on a smaller scale. The hamlet of Brooksbottom came into being when John Robinson Kay built his cotton mill at this water-power site in 1829. Whereas the Grants established a community of Presbyterians, the Kays created a hamlet of Wesleyan Methodists. They built a chapel, a school, and a few rows of cottages and, as Barton writes, "there soon gathered around this extensive works a thriving and happy colony of workpeople." Today it is hard to recapture the atmosphere of Lancashire at the start of the Industrial Revolution when scores of little colonies, centred on the new mills, were attracting far more immigrants than the fresh farms that settlers were breaking in the Canadian Lakes peninsula or amid the forests of the Old North-West beyond the Ohio River.

The large industrial towns of Lancashire were almost complete by the end of the nineteenth century. After 1900 the population curves show only a gentle rise, and the first World War is followed by a marked fall in total population, a trend that stands out most clearly in the textile towns so badly damaged by the slump of the 1930's. Oldham reached its maximum in 1911 with a total of 147,483. At the 1931 census it contained 140,314 people, and the last count in 1951 shows that the population has fallen back to a little over 120,000.

When the growth of population came to an end in Lancashire's industrial towns, the rows of cottages, new streets, chapels, and mills ceased to spread out

PLATE 25

A bleach-works near Bolton with a "lodge" in the foreground. In South-east Lancashire the mill often forms the core of an industrial hamlet.

into the green fields. Today these towns are museums of Victorian architecture, memorials of an age when Britain regarded the whole world as her market. Modern buildings only seem to fill in the gaps that were left when the towns stopped growing. The main shopping streets have the polished granite façades of the chain tailors and the chromium plate of the nation-wide furniture stores. The "super" cinemas are the largest contribution of the years of the great slump in the textile industry, their interior designs more in keeping with Palm Beach than Pendleton. The dreary avenues of municipal housing estates have been laid out since the first World War and the speculative builder has peppered the derelict land that surrounds many of the abandoned collieries with odd groups of "semis." They look curiously out of place with their latticed bay windows and meaningless flourishes of stained glass. Lancashire largely works in Victorian factories and governs itself from grim Gothic town halls. Yet even in the sphere of public buildings there are many exceptions to the view that urban Lancashire, as we see it today, is a product of the Victorians. Manchester has its new Central Library and Town Hall extension. Liverpool can proudly point to its Philharmonic Hall, the magnificent approach to the Mersey tunnel, and an Anglican Cathedral built in this century. At Wigan there is the Boys' Grammar School and Accrington has a modern Court House.

In the many Victorian histories of the Lancashire towns we can learn what our great-grandfathers felt about the places they were building. Everywhere there is a sense of pride in the new mills, the installation of bigger steam engines, and the laying out of fresh streets. Edwin Butterworth, the historian of Oldham, describes "the new power loom mill of Messrs. Radcliffe" which was opened in 1830. "The extent of the building and the noise of the busy throng form a scene equally curious and admirable. The workpeople appear to be most industrious, orderly and comfortable. A manufactory in such hands presents no unpleasant drawbacks on the feelings. The entire concern of Messrs. Radcliffe's spin about 45,000 pounds of cotton per week. In their mills upwards of 400,000 miles of cotton are produced in about sixty-six working hours. What an astonishing effect of the combination of mechanism! What an inconceivable wonder!"

Only occasionally do the local historians seem disturbed about the appearance of the new towns. Butterworth regretted the disappearance of the open heaths around Oldham, which were enclosed in 1807 and turned over to the speculative builders. In his description of Preston in 1820 Whittle hoped that some cure would be found for the pall of smoke that hung in the sky over the new factories, but nowhere does he write critically of the society that lived by the mills. Only the sensitive and the eccentric condemned the hell that had been made out of the garden of eighteenth-century England. Perhaps W. Cooke Taylor's account of Bolton in 1842 best sums up the feelings of the Victorians about industrial Lancashire. "Beyond is the hill on which a great part of the busy town of Bolton is built. The intervening valley is studded with factories and bleach works. Thank God, smoke is rising from the lofty chimneys of most of them! The smoke too creates no nuisance here—the chimneys are too far apart; and it produces variations in the atmosphere and sky which, to me at least, have a pleasing and picturesque effect."

The growth of the nineteenth-century town was not as chaotic as the present jumble of factories and our misconceptions about the Victorians might lead us to believe. Everywhere one can trace the development of small suburban centres that gradually become linked together in one town. In the 1790's Samuel Horrocks was building one mill after another on the eastern edge of Preston (Plate

26). The industrial suburb of New Preston arose in New Hall Lane Fields, where Horrocks built a spinning mill, hand-loom sheds, and long rows of cottages. For a long time New Preston was famous for its cock fighting, its poachers, and its heavy drinkers.

It was not only the addition of industrial suburbs that helped the manufacturing towns to grow to their present size and shape. The emergence of a large, comfortable middle class as a result of the widespread prosperity in the second half of the nineteenth century caused the growth of the appropriate middle-class suburb. Today we find its quiet streets and decaying red brick villas around Moor

PLATE 26

A prospect of Preston about 1830: the windmills and chimney-stacks show the market centre of the Fylde in the course of transformation into an industrial town.

Park in Preston and in the Swinley district of Wigan. For the first time the small mill-owner and the man with a good job in the office could afford to live out of sight of the factory. In his *Handbook and Guide to Preston* (1882) Pollard describes the creation of a residential suburb on the north bank of the Ribble towards Ashton. "Extensive tracts of arable and agricultural land have been laid out for building purposes, new streets and roads of considerable length intersecting each other at various points, and some hundreds of houses have already been erected, several of them of the villa class." In its greedy expansion Preston has now swallowed the village of Ashton.

The time when estates were developed affected the shape, street layout, and appearance of the towns. Edward Baines' *Directory* explains the patchwork building of Blackburn in 1825 by the fact that land owned by the parish church had not been developed: "the streets are irregularly built, partly owing to the intermixture of glebe and other lands, and partly to that eccentricity of taste and variety of convenience which generally prevail in manufacturing places." Ashton-under-Lyne provides an exception to the haphazard development that was the rule in Lancashire's towns. This large cotton-spinning centre grew up under the close supervision of the lords of the manor until it received a borough charter in 1847. From 1758 Ashton was the property of the Earls of Stamford. In 1750 Ashton consisted of "four narrow streets, formed by mean looking dwellings." During the next hundred years, while under the strict control of the Earls of Stamford, it grew into a thriving cotton town. The Earls' surveyors rigidly directed the siting of new property and the laying out of roads. As a result the modern map of Ashton shows a regular network of streets meeting at right-angles and at fixed distances apart, a grid-iron pattern resembling that of any city in the American Middle West (Plate 27).

Barrow-in-Furness arose in the second half of the nineteenth century on the estates of the Dukes of Devonshire. The dukes were directors and shareholders in the Furness Railway. They put their capital in the dock extensions, the making of Bessemer steel, the Iron Shipbuilding Company and the manufacture of jute. As lords of the manor they controlled the orderly development of the town. Standards of building were established and the width of roads dictated. Duke Street is 80 feet wide, and Abbey Road, the main entry into the town from the station, is a spacious tree-lined boulevard. Barrow and Ashton, with their directed growth and rigid grid-iron plans, are exceptions in the history of Lancashire's towns.

Apart from the development of private estates, a large amount of new building land came from the enclosure of the commons at the beginning of the nineteenth century. The Acts of Parliament for the enclosure of land form a thread in the history of eighteenth-century England coming to an end about 1840. They are the legal expression of one of the most sweeping transformations in the English landscape. In the Midlands these Acts of Parliament sanctioned the replacement of the great open fields by the neat, hedged enclosures that we see today. In Lancashire similar Acts of Parliament signalled the improvement and enclosure of the mosses; but perhaps the most striking visible change was the conversion of the open heaths, used for common grazing, into industrial suburbs tightly packed with mills and houses.

An Act of Parliament permitted the enclosure of the moors around Oldham in 1803. Up to that time a full circle of large open commons surrounded the parish church. Hollinwood Common lay to the south-west and covered more than sixty acres. To the north, on the poor rising ground of Oldham Edge, stretched Priest Hill Moor and North Moor. Eastwards, where the land rises high on the slopes of the Pennines, were extensive commons called High Moor, Sholver Moor, and

Greenacres Moor. When the enclosure commissioners finished their work in 1807 there was no doubt about the future ownership of the commons. The land was divided between the owners of property adjoining the waste. Thirty-nine landlords increased their estates with slices of Hollinwood Moor, and Sarah Moor passed into the hands of nineteen people.

When there were no longer any doubts about the right to develop the commons of Oldham they became the centre of speculative building. Edwin Butterworth has left a vivid picture of the transformation of Greenacres Moor after the commissioners had finished their task of dividing out the common land. "In 1807 the

PLATE 27

Ashton-under-Lyne about 1830: a town that developed with a grid-iron street-plan under the direction of the Earls of Stamford.

hundred acres of waste land had all been effectually reclaimed, and manufactories and habitations were all starting into existence as if by magic. At this latter period there were eight cotton mills, and nearly 236 houses, on the spot which thirty-six years before had been an almost uninhabited wilderness." By 1820 Butterworth reports ten cotton mills and almost 450 houses in Greenacres. In 1841 Greenacres formed the largest suburb of Oldham, a third of the built-up area of the town, with a population of 10,000 and twenty-three mills. Greenacres was one of the first industrial quarters of Oldham, and even today it stands out as a dense cluster of chimneys lying at the foot of the Pennines in the eastern parts of the town. Only its name commemorates the pleasant heath that was signed out of existence by an Act of Parliament.

The history of Preston Moor is different from that of the common lands in most of Lancashire's towns. The burgesses of Preston had acquired this stretch of waste from the royal forest of Fulwood in 1253 by a charter of Henry III. It was still an open, uncultivated heath in the eighteenth century, and provided the setting for the Corporation horse races from 1786 to 1833. Preston Moor was enclosed in 1834 by a resolution of the Corporation. It did not pass into the hands of the promoters of the new industrial suburbs, but remained in the possession of the Corporation, which constructed an avenue with lodges at its eastern and western ends. The Moor remained as a piece of rough heath until 1867, when

PLATE 28

Allotments, terraced houses, and cotton mills at Shaw, near Oldham. With the rise of the industrial towns Lancashire too often exchanged her heaths and open commons for tiny allotments and hen-runs.

it was converted into a public park with an ornamental lake, gravel walks, pavilions, and flower beds. The transformation of Preston Moor into a Victorian park came from the need to find work for the unemployed in the cotton famine, when the stoppage of raw cotton from the United States during the American Civil War brought the Lancashire textile industry to a standstill.

Preston owes the preservation of its common land at the time of enclosure to the strength of its corporation. The borough had enjoyed a powerful local government since the early Middle Ages, but in the new industrial towns there was no strong public body to enforce the community's claim to the enclosed commons.

Some of their citizens felt very strongly about it. At a public dinner in 1853 James Platt, one of the members of the great engineering partnership of Hibbert and Platt, spoke of the wrongs done to Oldham by the enclosure award of 1803. "If there had been a local government authority of municipal status much of the common land might have become the property of the town. . . . If the land had come into the possession of the town there would have been no need to levy a rate for the expense of its improvement and management."

PLATE 29

Oldham from the air: the functional cubes of the spinning mills, the regular rows of the terraced houses with gleaming window sills, and the sombre mill-dams make up the pattern of the Victorian industrial town.

The industrial towns did not grow steadily and smoothly through the nineteenth century until they reached their present shape and size about 1910 (Plate 29). They expanded by a series of jumps, sprouting new suburbs when the mills were booming, languishing when the textile industry struggled in a slump. Edwin Butterworth has left a vigorous sketch of the effect of a short period of prosperity on Oldham in the early 1820's, when trade began to revive after the slump that followed the end of the Napoleonic Wars. "New cotton manufactories and a great number of dwelling-houses rapidly increased. The manufacturers of houses and mills were as eager speculators as those of goods and yarn. The town was indebted for many of its new buildings, enlarged factories, and steam engine establishments, entirely to this age of paper money." . . . "During the ascendancy of such a spirit, streets were in many instances run up on every side as fast, if not faster than tenants could be found, hence the sudden enlargement of the town on every hand, owing to the work of speculating builders, clever lawyers, and money-making bankers, who were of course anxious to make five per cent. of their credit."

High prosperity and the mushroom growth of new streets and mills was followed by depression and biting poverty. The 1841 census shows that unemployment forced workers to leave the textile towns of South-east Lancashire. Butterworth reports that Oldham had 1,800 empty houses in 1840 and starvation drove several families together to live under one roof. Chartism was at its height, and the Reverend J. R. Stephens, a Methodist minister from Ashton-under-Lyne, whose thick, square-cut beard made him look the most prim and proper of Victorians, addressed a crowd of 3,000 at an open meeting in Oldham with the words "blow out the brains of your masters and pull down their bastilles."

The 1870's started another long period of prosperity in the cotton towns, perhaps the steadiest in the history of the industry. In 1875 the factory inspector reported that thirty-two new cotton mills had been built within four miles of Oldham town hall. Many of the great five- and six-storey mills, huge tiers of glass, glazed brick and terra cotta that litter the forlorn landscape between Manchester and Oldham, were built in this boom period at the close of the nineteenth century. The feverish floating of new companies and the rapidly expanding population is reflected by the opening of fifteen new churches and chapels in Oldham between 1870 and 1885.

Apart from the effect of changing prosperity on the growth of towns, the foundation of a new industry often caused a new suburb to spring into life. Leach's account of Barrow-in-Furness (1872) shows how the founding of the Iron Shipbuilding Company in 1870 converted Old Barrow Island into an industrial quarter. "Old Barrow Island—two years since quite a pleasant rural nook, with fields of waving grain and blooming hedgerows—has been transformed with almost magical rapidity into a teeming hive of industry. Around the gigantic works, within which the sound of the smiths' and riveters' hammers is already beginning to re-echo, has grown up quite a little town of wooden houses, constructed for the temporary accommodation of workmen until a sufficient number of brick dwellings shall have been provided by the extensive building operations which are going on all round the town of Barrow."

In 1896 Vickers Sons and Company bought the Barrow shipyard and three years later they started to build "a marine garden city" on Walney Island. Vickerstown contained 930 houses in 1904. A bridge was built across the Walney Channel in 1908 and the new residential suburb became part of Barrow. Six hundred and ten houses were added to Vickerstown with the vast influx of

PLATE 30

Shaw: the shapeless creation of the cotton boom of the 1870's.

workers to Barrow's engineering industries in the first World War. The building of a whole suburb at the expense of one firm takes us a long way from the chaotic development of the textile towns at the beginning of the nineteenth century. The neat rows of cottages in Vickerstown, the orderly streets curving over the gentle slopes of the clay hill that forms one of the ribs of Walney Island, and "planned amenities" like the King Alfred Hotel and The George, are a foretaste of the new towns of our own time.

Churches and Chapels

The nineteenth century was the age of ecclesiastical architecture in Lancashire. At the Reformation the county had only fifty-eight parish churches. By 1915 it contained 896 parishes, many of them with more than one church. In lowland England clusters of churches of roughly the same date and displaying fine architectural features often point to a distant period of economic prosperity. Some of the best churches in Northamptonshire's stone belt were built in a period of prosperity that drew to a close about the end of the thirteenth century. In Cornwall there is almost a surfeit of elegant granite towers dating from the fifteenth and early sixteenth centuries. Lancashire likewise has a memorial to its century of prosperous and expanding trade in its hundreds of Victorian churches, a grim Gothic revival that is not out of place amid the forests of chimney stacks and grey canals.

None of the churches in the industrial towns—save Manchester Cathedral, a splendid Perpendicular church—has survived intact and unrestored from the centuries before 1800; to avoid the craft of the Victorian renovator one must turn to the small market towns and villages. Blackburn, Rochdale, Bolton, Ashton, and several of the manufacturing towns have had churches since the early Middle Ages, but as a rule they were pulled down and completely rebuilt in the last century or so much restored and enlarged that the early fragments are only of interest to the antiquarian. St. Chad's, Rochdale, is typical of the old parish churches in the industrial towns. When the town was growing rapidly in 1815 the parishioners decided to restore the church rather than build afresh in the style of the Gothic Revival. At a second restoration in 1885 the chancel was rebuilt in the heavy romantic fashion favoured by the Victorians, but the lower parts of the tower survive from the thirteenth and fourteenth centuries.

In many towns a clean break was made with the past, and the old parish church that harmonized with the life of the village or small market centre was replaced by a huge monument to the Gothic Revival; its heavy stained-glass windows, presented by wealthy manufacturers, shut out the grim view of the enveloping chimneys. Peter Ormrod, a rich cotton spinner and banker, put up the money for a completely new parish church at Bolton in 1867. It was designed by E. G. Paley, the Lancaster architect who left his mark on so many of Lancashire's towns. When the site was cleared for the new church three fragments of a decorated cross, dating from the ninth century, were found underneath the tower, suggesting that Bolton had a church before the Norman Conquest. At

Ashton-under-Lyne the parish church was twice demolished and rebuilt within fifty years, first in 1844 and again in 1888.

Amid the vast disorderly expansion of Lancashire's towns one can recognize three predominant periods of church building. The first came in the 1830's, when Parliament provided funds for churches in the new manufacturing suburbs. St. Clements, Rochdale, was built with money from the "Million grant" in 1835 on a site presented by the prosperous cotton spinner, James Royds. A second period of church building occurs in the years about 1850 (Plate 31), when many of the smaller outlying industrial settlements became separate parishes. Christ

PLATE 31

St. Thomas's Church at Wigan: a church and Sunday school of the 1850's, a period when many new parishes were created in the Lancashire industrial towns.

Church, Healey, was built in 1850 on a bench above the deep valley of the Spoddon, two miles from Rochdale. Belmont, an industrial village, hemmed in by the sepia-coloured moors, with a drab string of gritstone cottages standing above a line of bleach works, saw the consecration of St. Peter's in the same year.

Many new churches were built in a third phase between 1870 and 1890. At this stage two styles of architecture can be clearly distinguished. There are the simple, inexpensive buildings of the working-class suburbs and the costly, ornate churches of the comfortable residential districts. Rochdale has good examples of both kinds. St. Peter's Church, Newbold, was finished in 1871 in an industrial district between the Rochdale Canal and the Lancashire and Yorkshire Railway. Robertson's *Rochdale Past and Present* (1875) describes its "pointed Gothic style of a bold and vigorous type." "Stock brick is introduced in the coigns, bands, strings, buttresses, and arches, in the ornamental panels, mouldings and cornices, and in other places where dressed stone is more usually employed. It cost £4,000 and has seating for 650." St. Edmund's Church, Falinge, a fashionable suburb of middle-class villas, was consecrated in 1873. It cost £20,000, and the capital was found by Albert Hudson Royds, a member of one of the leading industrial families in Rochdale. The church is filled with that bizarre and luxurious decoration beloved by the comfortable Victorians. Robertson describes the square tower "rising from the transept, supported by four columns of Aberdeen granite; above the capitals are designs representing fruit and foliage of the four seasons." The south window "is considered to be a marvel of artistic execution" and was on view at the Vienna Exhibition of 1873.

The creation of nonconformist chapels in the Lancashire towns was a more complex process than the founding of Anglican churches. The new parishes of the Church of England were directly related to the expanding population. Besides responding to the physical growth of the towns the nonconformist churches often grew rapidly as they won over new converts, perhaps under the influence of some flamboyant preacher or the zealous crusade of a band of Sunday-school teachers. New chapels and ephemeral sects arose out of doctrinal differences or the bitter quarrels over the management of Sunday schools and chapels.

Rochdale has an exciting history of break-away communities among her nonconformists. Providence Chapel in High Street arose in 1806 from a personal and doctrinal quarrel in the Methodist Connexion. The Methodists objected to their minister, the Reverend Joseph Cooke, and expelled him from the church. A group of supporters followed him into his doctrinal wilderness and collected money to build the Providence Chapel. When their minister died in 1814 the little community drifted back into the Methodist Church, and Providence was put up for sale. The Congregationalists bought it for £1,600 and built "an ornamental portico that added considerably to its exterior effect."

More often than not the view along the sombre streets of industrial Lancashire is closed by the façade of a nonconformist chapel (Plate 32). Their architectural styles are as varied as the histories of many of these little sects. The Wellington Road Primitive Methodist Chapel, Bury, was built "in a plain, substantial, Italian style of architecture under the personal supervision of the Reverend J. Mould." At Belmont the congregation constructed the Bethel Chapel with their own hands in 1840. In 1872 a group of Welshmen established a Welsh Calvinistic Methodist Chapel in Bolton, and in the 1840's missionaries from the Middle West were able to found a sect of Mormons in Wigan. At St. Helens the Friends Meeting House comes as a shock when you walk through the main street of the town, thronged with trolley buses and flanked by the garish chromium-plated shop fronts of the cheap furniture stores. The Meeting House has scarcely changed since the day it was built in the seventeenth century. It stands back across a grey-green lawn, its dark Billinge sandstone and heavy roof of stone slates preserving a relic of the countryside that was there before the town was built.

Public Buildings

A walk through the streets of a Lancashire mill town reveals two distinct styles of Victorian architecture. On the one hand there are the acres of grimy terraced houses, the plain brick chapels, and the clean functional outlines of the mills. In

PLATE 32

Haslingden: a chapel seems to close the view at the end of every street in the industrial towns of Rossendale. The quarries that scar the hillsides above the town have provided stone for pavements, cobbles and terraces of houses in this scene.

opposition to this utilitarian style we find the ornate and highly decorated town halls, museums, libraries, swimming baths, and municipal offices. They represent two phases of urban history in the nineteenth century. Before 1870, few public buildings, apart from churches and chapels, were erected in the industrial towns. In this period a school or working men's hall was the result of an individual gift or the chance effort of a group of people with some special idea in mind. For instance, in 1810 the eccentric and wealthy Oldham hat-manufacturer, Thomas Henshaw, drowned himself in a mill dam and left £40,000 to build a Bluecoat School. The appearance of strong local government in the second half of the nineteenth century with the right to levy rates for public works and the elementary legislation of the welfare state introduced a wave of public building in every large town. The new board schools, technical colleges, libraries, museums, swimming baths, fire stations, and huge Gothic town halls all date from this second period.

Lancashire's town halls range from a pleasant classical style through poor examples of "domestic Gothic" to enormous buildings with decorated towers and spires, elaborate models of the late medieval *hôtels de villes* of Flanders. The commissioners who governed Oldham before the town received its charter in 1848 erected an attractive classical town hall in 1841. It is one of the earliest public buildings in the town and might easily have been destroyed when a huge, dull extension was added to the original building in 1879—a time when Oldham was expanding at an astonishing pace. The plain little building of 1841 reflects an age when stern individualism resented any expenditure of money for civic purposes.

Oldham Town Hall cost £4,000. The great Gothic "hôtel de ville" at Rochdale, opened in 1872, cost £155,000. W. H. Crossland, a Leeds architect, designed Rochdale Town Hall as an epitome in stone, stained glass, and carved wood of the life and values of Victorian England. Robertson, in *Rochdale Past and Present* (1875), devotes a whole chapter to a detailed description of the building. With a tower and spire 240 feet in height: "it is a handsome Gothic edifice, so richly ornamented as not inappropriately to have been compared to a cathedral." A succession of stained-glass windows illustrates the cotton industry "with cotton pods and leaves and the machinery used in its manufacture." In the Mayor's reception room "every bit of space had been more or less beautified by the decorator's art." "The beams have illustrations on a gold ground of seven of Æsop's fables." Where the beams join the wall they are "supported by four sculptured figures, which were intended for grotesque likenesses of the then mayor, Alderman George L. Ashworth, with the Town Hall in his hand, Mr. W. H. Crossland the architect, an alderman in his gown (Mr. E. Taylor) and a councillor (Mr. W. A. Scott)." The windows of the Council Chamber contained the arms of the Duke of Bridgewater, Sir Richard Arkwright, and Sir Robert Peel, "men who have materially assisted by their intelligence and active interest the progress made in the textile industry." The stained-glass windows of the Exchange showed "the arms of the continental nations who are regarded as the best customers of the manufacturers of Rochdale." We can hardly share the wonder of the Victorians at this Gothic palace—"by gas light the Great Hall assumes the aspect of some magnificent oriental temple"—but we can preserve it as one of the best memorials of an age when Lancashire found its market in the whole world and hoped to achieve the brotherhood of man through international trade.

Many of Lancashire's boroughs built their town halls in the favourable economic climate of the years between 1870 and 1890. In 1879 St. Helens opened its new town hall designed by Sumner, the Liverpool architect. At Barrow-in-Furness they used the red sandstone from local quarries and a style less extravagant than Rochdale's. Waterhouse was the architect of Manchester Town Hall, opened in

1877. Murray's *Handbook for Lancashire* (1880) sums up this monument to a time when Manchester believed herself to be the first city of the Empire, at least for all the serious and important things in life. "The stranger should notice the vaulted corridors, the crypt-like vestibules, the winding staircases all studded with Gothic ornament and elaborate tracery, and hundreds of columns of polished marble and granite." In the 1930's, when the slump closed down scores of cotton mills and vast quantities of machinery went to the scrap-metal merchants, Manchester faced the problem of designing an extension to its huge Gothic town hall. Waterhouse's fantastic palace now extends round the eastern arc of the new Central Library in a towering, austere annexe of Portland stone, a chilly architectural reminder of a change in the economic climate.

As we wander round Barrow, St. Helens, or Oldham, and remember that the oldest of these towns was built within the last century and a half, it is hard to believe that they have a history. They look as though they were designed and built all in one piece. Yet every street and building has a local history closely connected with men whose ideas and lives are already hard for us to understand. Already many streets in Lancashire's mill towns have passed through more than one cycle of history—their buildings have been destroyed and rebuilt more than once in the past century.

There are bleak open spaces and barren spoil heaps in the heart of St. Helens where the chemical works used to belch their poisonous fumes. The whole industry was concentrated on Widnes after the first World War, when the manufacture of chemicals was replanned on a national scale. The main street of Preston, Fishergate, was almost completely rebuilt in the 1870's. Pollard's *Handbook and Guide to Preston* (1882) describes its transformation from a residential district to the main commercial and shopping street of the town. "Within the last few years this thoroughfare may be said to have undergone an entire transformation, having been converted from a locality consisting very largely of private dwellings into a busy and active emporium of trade and commerce; the private residences of the oldest and best families have become shops, hotels and business premises."

Tontine Street was the most fashionable part of St. Helens in the 1820's. Today it is one of the most depressing sights in Lancashire. There is a patch of waste ground where Daglish's iron foundry once stood—a firm of engineers that designed railways for the United States, built a bridge across the Liffey, and helped in the construction of the Liverpool docks. On one side of Tontine Street a patched and shapeless fence shuts off the yards of warehouses, on the other stands a wall formed from the fronts of a demolished row of cottages with a regular succession of bricked-up doorways and projecting window-sills. As you stand in this junk heap of industrialism it is hard to believe that scarcely a century ago this was the best street in St. Helens.

Ports and Seaside Towns

Nature has determined that the ports of Lancashire should be situated on the

Mersey and Ribble estuaries and along the shores of Morecambe Bay. Today, Liverpool, second port of the British Isles, has eaten the life out of all the other harbours in the county. Two centuries ago Liverpool was still Lancashire's biggest port, thriving on the Atlantic trade in tobacco, sugar, cotton, and slaves, but there were also several prosperous small harbours that have now lost all contact with the sea.

Sunderland and Glasson Dock face each other across the mouth of the Lune, wrapped around by green fields with the chimneys of Lancaster's linoleum works on the distant horizon. Sunderland, on the north side of the river, became a busy

PLATE 33

Sunderland: a port at the mouth of the Lune that prospered on the West Indian trade in the first decades of the eighteenth century.

trading centre in the early years of the eighteenth century under the directing genius of Robert Lawson, a Quaker merchant from Lancaster. William Stout, another Lancaster Quaker, tells in his diary of the bankruptcy of Robert Lawson in 1728. "He had done as much in merchandize here as all the rest, and had good success in trade, but employed the profit in superfluity of buying land at great prices, and building chargeable and unnecessary houses, barns, gardens, and other fancies, and costly furniture; so that he overshot himself. . . ." The final laconic phrase could be an epitaph on Sunderland, where some of Lawson's warehouses stand abandoned in the fields that come down to the salt-marsh and the water's edge.

Sunderland decayed after 1750 (Plate 33) and was replaced by the better anchorage at Glasson on the south bank of the Lune, where the Lancaster port commissioners equipped a wet dock for twenty-five merchant ships in 1791. Glasson commemorates an attempt to create a great port at the mouth of the Lune. It recalls a brief period of heavy capital investment when the merchants of Lancaster stood at the height of their prosperity, before Liverpool grabbed all the trade of the Atlantic and before the ports of Fleetwood, Heysham, and Barrow had entered the imagination. Glasson, unlike Sunderland, has not dropped all contact with the sea. A rusty tramp steamer occasionally lies in the dock basin waiting for the scrap-metal merchant. Up on Tithe Barn Hill old men and children sit about and stare across the expanse of Morecambe Bay, out beyond the dark smudge of Rossall Point, for a sight of the cork boat that will bring a cargo to the Lancaster linoleum mills and animate the empty quays of Glasson Dock for a few hours.

Since its foundation as a borough in 1207 Liverpool has kept its position as Lancashire's greatest port. It is easy to find an obvious explanation for this in the shape of the Mersey estuary, a great glittering lake whose ebb-tide runs through the jetty at New Brighton like a boisterous mill-race, helping to keep clear the deep-water channel of the river. But if we only remember this geographical fact we neglect the energy of the people of this city who have adjusted their lives to a whole succession of historical events and economic situations.

Until the middle of the seventeenth century the town of Liverpool was confined to a peninsula between the Mersey and a quiet creek, the Pool, that stretched inland for half a mile. The trade of medieval Liverpool was mainly with Ireland. King John embarked men and supplies from the Pool for his Irish campaign in 1209. In the fourteenth century it was again a military port for the Scottish and Irish Wars of Edward III. Apart from the traffic of war there was always the trade in wool, cloth, cattle, and hides. Leland, writing in Henry VIII's reign, explains Liverpool's early success as a port: "Irish merchants come much thither, as to a good haven. . . . At Liverpool is small custom paid that causeth merchants to resort. Good merchandize at Liverpool; and much Irish yarn, that Manchester men do buy there."

The population of medieval Liverpool was probably about 1,000. A burgess roll of 1346 records 196 householders in the town. The hearth tax return of 1673 records 252 householders in Liverpool, which suggests a population of about 1,500. There were still only six streets in the whole town. In no sense could old Liverpool be matched against great commercial and industrial towns like Coventry, Norwich, Bristol, or Exeter.

Liverpool expanded rapidly in the eighteenth century with the development of the African and American trade. Daniel Defoe described the town as "one of the wonders of Britain. What it may grow in time, I know not." It is estimated that Liverpool's population rose from 5,000 to 18,000 in the first half of the eighteenth century. By 1708 the ancient pool from which it took its name had been filled in and streets spread over it. The six streets had grown to thirty-four; and by 1725 another sixteen streets had been built. A plan made in 1766 shows about 166 streets in being. A metropolis was emerging on the Lancashire coast.

Between 1709 and 1715 the first of the long chain of docks that flanks the north shore of the Mersey was constructed in the mouth of the Pool by Thomas Steers, Liverpool's first dock engineer. In 1734 Steers started to build Salthouse Dock on the open shore. It took nineteen years to complete and represents one of the first triumphs of the engineers of the Industrial Revolution in Lancashire. With these transformations of the north bank of the Mersey, the Pool, the most striking feature of the geography of medieval Liverpool, was finally wiped off the map. Today the site of the medieval town betrays itself in the irregularity of the street-plan between the shore at Pierhead and Whitechapel on the site of the Pool.

Liverpool became a great city and a world port in the early part of the nineteenth century. The trade of the Indian Ocean was thrown open in 1813 and Liverpool started to develop the market in India for Lancashire's cotton goods. The foundation of the Cunard Line in 1842 started the first regular service of passenger ships across the Atlantic. The dingy streets and shoddy tenements of the town spread untidily inland in an effort to house a continuous stream of immigrants from Ireland and Wales, and a huge line of docks grew along the Mersey waterfront.

The Liverpool docks are one of Lancashire's greatest memorials to the energy of the nineteenth century. They stand behind a massive granite river wall, thrust out into the Mersey over a length of seven miles. The successive opening of new docks roughly mirrors the expansion of Liverpool's traffic, just as the increasing size of the sheets of quiet grey water in the dock basins reflects the sudden growth in the size of ships in the 1880's. The Clarence, Waterloo, Victoria, and Trafalgar docks were opened in the 1830's. The site of the Clarence Dock is now occupied by the power station that stands on the river front, where a sombre flight of locks falls from the Leeds and Liverpool Canal between the precipitous walls of the warehouses.

The year 1848 was notable in the history of Liverpool, when the Stanley, Collingwood, Salisbury, Nelson, and Bramley Moore docks were all opened. At this time, before Southampton began to compete in the Atlantic traffic, Liverpool almost monopolized the trade with North America. In the first three months of 1846 over 90,000 migrants reached Liverpool from Ireland. Between July 1847 and July 1848 more than 300,000 Irish entered the town. Most of them went on to America, but a remnant which could not face or finance the journey across the Atlantic found work in the slums of Liverpool, or in the rising glass and chemical industries of St. Helens and Widnes. Four great docks were added at Bootle in the 1880's, and the monumental river wall was completed in 1927 on the sands at Seaforth with the opening of the Gladstone Dock.

Lancaster, like Liverpool, flourished on the West Indian trade, but she enjoyed only two generations of high prosperity, between about 1750 and 1800. A century earlier Lancaster was scarcely known as a port. Defoe, who had been struck with wonder at the sight of the thriving town of Liverpool, found little to interest him in Lancaster. "The town is ancient; it lies, as it were, in its own ruins, and has little to recommend it but a decayed castle, and a more decayed port." He little realized that the closing decades of the eighteenth century would see a stream of ships from the West Indies, unloading their cargoes of sugar, rum, and mahogany in front of the severe grey warehouses on St. George's Quay. Out of their wealth the Lancaster merchants, many of them Quakers, rebuilt their "ruined town." In his *Six Months Tour through the North of England* (1770) Arthur Young reports more than a hundred ships at Lancaster trading with Africa and America; and "the cabinet makers work up mahogany brought home in their own ships and re-export it to the West Indies." "It is a town that increases in buildings; having many new piles, much superior to the old streets, and handsomely raised of white stone and slates."

A stroll through Lancaster today is very satisfying, for the town has escaped the blight of the Industrial Revolution. There is the same sense of unity that one finds in Chipping Campden, Lavenham, and Truro. Dickens felt the power of its history when he saw the gaunt, grey merchants' houses of Lancaster: "and Mr. Goodchild adds that the stones of Lancaster do sometimes whisper, even yet, of rich men passed away—upon whose great prosperity some of these old doorways frowned sullen in the brightest weather—that their slave gain turned to curses . . ." (*The Lazy Tour of Two Idle Apprentices*).

The most perfect piece of Lancaster is St. George's Quay, where Richard Gillow designed and built the Custom House in 1764. It looks across the muddy channel of the Lune at low tide, commemorating a family that played a vital part in the shaping of the town. Robert Gillow, who is recorded in the Freemen Rolls of Lancaster in 1727 as a "joyner" making coffins, pig troughs, and mangles, was one of the founders of the furniture industry. About 1740 he started to buy tropical hardwoods and exported heavy mahogany furniture for the homes of planters in the Sugar Isles. He named his workshops after the markets where he sold his goods—Barbadoes, San Domingo, and St. Helena. In the 1770's Richard Gillow was building many of the fine houses that still adorn Lancaster's streets. The evolution of his family from making pig troughs to organizing a world trade in high-quality furniture epitomizes the history of his native town.

The seaside towns of Lancashire grew up during the nineteenth century on the blunt exposed peninsulas between the muddy estuaries. Morecambe started its career as a resort when the craze for sea-bathing swept over the English upper classes. In 1821 the *Lancaster Gazette* advertised "Sea bathing to Let—Morecambe Cottage at Poulton by the Sands." At the same time the Ship Inn at Sunderland, the decayed port at the mouth of the Lune, advertised its bathing machine. It was a serious rival for Morecambe. Both Sunderland and Poulton (the name Morecambe only became established after the building of the railway) organized regattas on successive days in July 1829. The *Lancaster Gazette* wrote on July 25 that the Poulton regatta "was numerously and fashionably attended." This paper always wrote of Morecambe in glowing terms, and probably contributed a lot to the growth of the resort before 1850. "On arriving on the ground we were struck with peculiar pleasure on viewing this village, presenting a maritime situation, which we think would now vie with some of the most celebrated watering places in the kingdom. . . . Some spirited gentlemen of this town have erected some beautiful and excellent houses which when we take into consideration their situation, and the commanding and extensive views they present on every side of the bay, the distant hills of the Lake scenery, we think we may justly predict, that this, in a very little time, will be the most fashionable resort in the neigh-

PLATE 34

St. George's Quay: the commercial centre of eighteenth-century Lancaster with its austere grey warehouses of local stone.

bourhood." In a century that was destined to read Ruskin, to revel in Gothic architecture and romantic scenery, Morecambe with its blue panorama of distant mountains, set out across the shimmering foreground of the bay, stood a good chance of becoming the fashionable resort of the north-west.

The building of railways between 1844 and 1850 established a hinterland for Morecambe in the industrial towns of Lancashire and Yorkshire. It abandoned its prospects as a resort of fashion and developed alongside Blackpool as a seaside town for the working classes. When the railway was opened through the Lune valley to the woollen towns of the West Riding in 1850, the first excursion trains ran into Morecambe. The *Lancaster Gazette* reports an outing of 300 Sunday-school children from Austwick and Clapham on June 22, 1850; and a few days later a mill trip from Preston filled the resort.

Fleetwood is perhaps the most fascinating of Lancashire's seaside towns (Fig. 9). Unlike Southport, Blackpool, and Morecambe, it did not grow casually out of a taste for sea-bathing and seaside holidays, but was deliberately planned by the owner of Rossall Hall, Sir Peter Hesketh-Fleetwood. It has been suggested that the idea of a town on the barren warren at the mouth of the Wyre came to him while he watched the opening ceremonies of the Liverpool and Manchester Railway in 1830.[1] One can imagine that such a display of the technical achievements of the age might stir a grandiose project in town planning.

At Preston in 1834 there was a meeting to raise capital for a railway to the mouth of the Wyre. In 1836 Decimus Burton, the architect of the new town of Fleetwood, marked out the position of the first streets with a plough. Sir Peter aimed to build a fashionable resort after the style of St. Leonards-on-Sea. He chose Decimus Burton, the student of John Nash and designer of the lodges in Hyde Park and the Screen and Triumphal Arch at the head of Constitution Hill, to carry out his scheme.

Fleetwood showed little immediate profit. In 1842 Sir Peter had to abandon his experiment in town planning with his own finances in ruins. The town fell into the control of mortgagees and they dismissed the master-architect, Decimus Burton. Fleetwood grew spasmodically after the financial crisis of 1842. Its career as a resort seemed to be finished by the opening of the railway to Blackpool in 1846. Under the influence of Benjamin Whitworth, a Manchester textile manufacturer and M.P. for the Fylde, Fleetwood started to import cotton in 1857, a trade that was soon snuffed out by the American Civil War and the Cotton Famine. The Lancashire and Yorkshire Railway opened a new dock in 1878 and the improvement in trade caused a fresh wave of building in the town. In 1892 a Grimsby firm established a trawler fishing fleet on the Wyre and started the transformation of Fleetwood into the largest fishing port on the west coast of Britain. After 1900 it once again emerged as a resort, joining Lytham and St. Anne's in capturing the holiday traffic that spilled over from Blackpool.

As we walk through the streets of Fleetwood today the financial crisis of 1842 stands before us in the building styles of the town. The cool, clear conception of a town, the work of the last great architect of the English classical school, is preserved in the street plan. Decimus Burton devised a radial plan focused on a high dune among the confused sand-hills at the tip of the Rossall peninsula. Today, the unusually wide streets, suggesting the sense of space of its classical architect, radiate from the Mount in a three-quarter circle. Several of Decimus Burton's buildings survive to show what Fleetwood might have been (Plate 35). There is the dignified curved façade of the North Euston Hotel, and the Custom House that now serves as the town hall. Queens Terrace faces the station, a row of eight houses in the style of Burton's work around Regent's Park. He also built

[1]Hesketh, *Sir Peter Hesketh-Fleetwood, Founder of the town and port of Fleetwood.*

the two lighthouses that contribute an individual flavour to the landscape of this unexciting fishing port. But, for the rest, Fleetwood might be part of any Lancashire town with its characterless terraces and Victorian villas in glazed brick.

The strain of financing his new town forced Sir Peter Hesketh-Fleetwood to sell his other estates in Lancashire. Ironically enough they included the part of the Fylde coast where Blackpool was to emerge as a great resort, and the manor of North Meols that was to become Southport. In 1840 he sold the Blackpool property; and in the following year the Southport estate passed into another

PLATE 35

Classical Fleetwood: Decimus Burton's lighthouse and the portico of the North Euston hotel.

branch of the family. In 1844 Sir Peter left Rossall Hall, his country house near to Fleetwood, and let it to the new North of England Public School.

William Hutton, the remarkable Birmingham topographer, wrote the first account of Blackpool as a seaside resort. His *Description of Blackpool in Lancashire, frequented for sea-bathing* (1789) presents a picture of the resort as he saw it at the very beginning of its astonishing career. At that time Blackpool was a dispersed settlement facing the fresh westerly winds from its site along the top of a low line of boulder clay cliffs. "The bank or cliff, which is clay, rises various heights, from three feet to sixty above high-water mark. Although about fifty houses

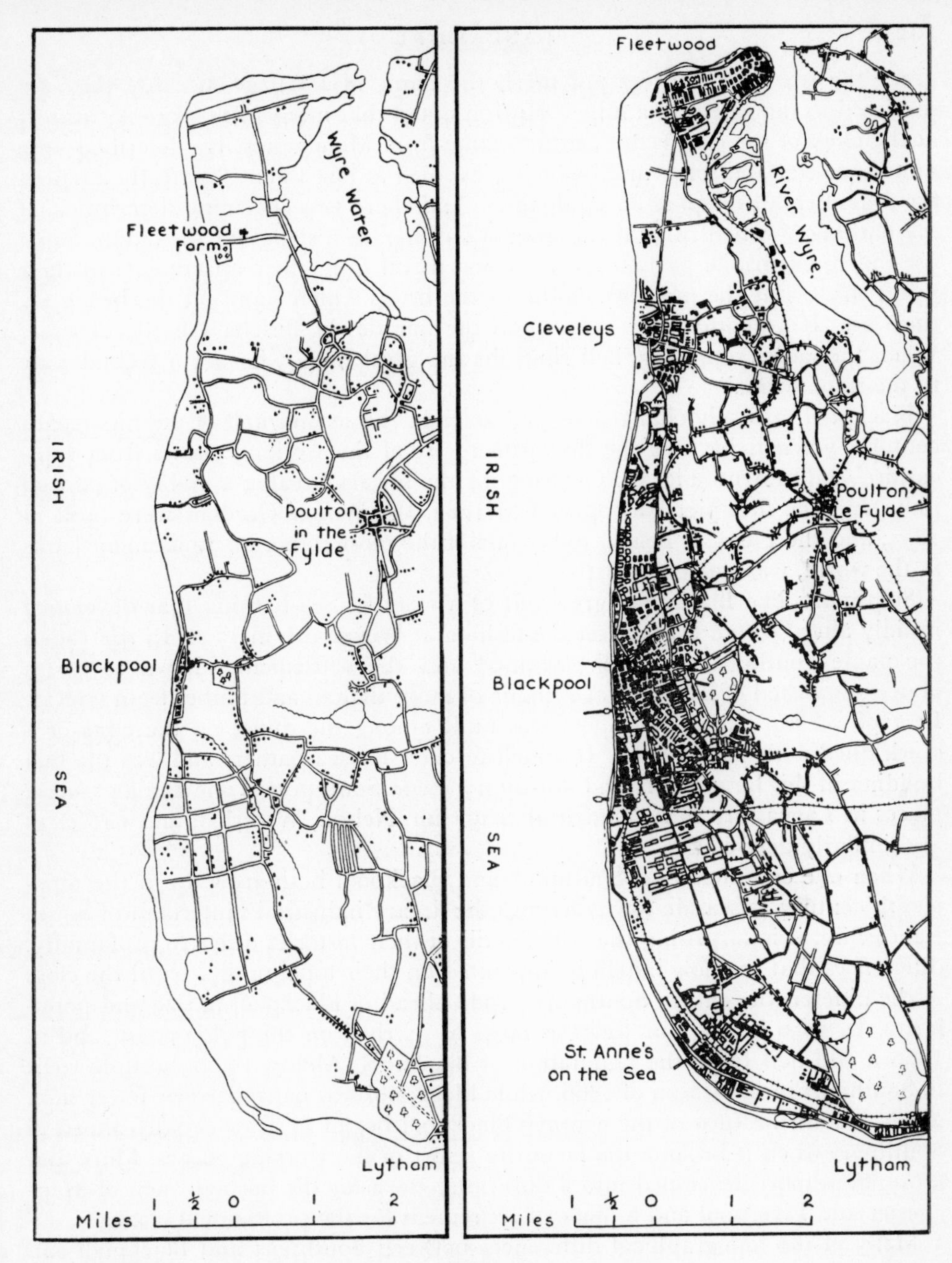

FIG. 9

The Fylde coast: 1828 and 1946. Blackpool was a string of villas facing the sea from the top of a low clay cliff when Hennet made his survey for Teesdale's map in 1828-9. Fleetwood was only a solitary farm. The modern map shows the transformation of Blackpool into the largest seaside resort in the north of England and the emergence of three other coastal towns: Fleetwood, Cleveleys, and St. Anne's.

grace the sea bank, it does not merit the name of a village, because they are scattered to the extent of a mile." Hutton noted that many of Blackpool's visitors at the close of the eighteenth century came from Manchester. He described "the most beautiful and solid sand" which is exposed at low water, "perfectly adapted for a gentleman to sport an equipage." And there is a charming description of sea-bathing. "A bell rings at the time of bathing, as a signal for the ladies. Some use machines drawn by one horse. A few travel from their apartments in their water dress; but the majority clothe in the boxes which stand on the beach for their use. If a gentleman is seen upon the parade, he forfeits a bottle of wine. When the ladies retire, the bell rings for the gentlemen, who act a second part in the same scene."

Blackpool radically changed its character in the second half of the nineteenth century, when it became the favourite resort of the working classes from Lancashire's mill towns (Fig. 9). Catering for the masses became a highly organized industry. The first pier was opened in 1863, the Winter Gardens were built in 1875, and the Pleasure Beach, today one of the most elaborate amusement parks in the world, was started in 1910.

Southport, like Blackpool, grew out of a taste for sea-bathing that developed rapidly after George III had set the fashion at Weymouth in 1798. In the 1790's the name Southport was still uncoined and the settlement, known as South Hawes, consisted of a few cottages made of mud, thatch, and timber from wrecks. In 1798 an inn called Southport was built among the dunes on the edge of a creek filled with salt-marshes. It aimed to cater for sea-bathers and was the first building in this large resort and dormitory town. Southport is one among several places in Lancashire to be named after an inn. Nelson, Waterloo, and Cleveleys are similarly derived.

When one considers that Southport and Blackpool both grew up in the nineteenth century as seaside towns serving the dreary industrial hinterland of South Lancashire, it is surprising that the details of their histories differ so profoundly, differences that are now indelibly imprinted on their topography. Until the close of the nineteenth century Southport strode ahead of Blackpool in size and popularity. In 1850 it was four times as large as its rival on the Fylde coast, and in 1890 it still had twice the population of Blackpool. Almost 10,000 visitors went to Southport in the season of 1866, while Blackpool was patronized by fewer than 2,000. About the turn of the century Blackpool began to draw rapidly ahead of Southport when it became the favourite resort of the working classes. More and more, Southport developed into a dormitory town for the business men of Manchester and Liverpool and a place of retirement for the professional classes.

Many of the topographical differences between Southport and Blackpool can be explained by the ownership of land and the terms of building leases. The manor of North Meols, in which Southport arose, belonged to two families, the Hesketh and the Bolds. The lords of the manor, who were responsible for the development of the resort until the granting of a borough charter in 1867, strictly controlled the development of Southport. They determined the chequer-board plan of wide tree-lined streets, and the leases under which houses were built forbade the construction of terraces and insisted that they should be placed in spacious gardens. In their desire for space and order they were creating the first and only "garden city" in Lancashire.

The disposal of the estates at Blackpool in 1840 during Sir Peter Hesketh-Fleetwood's financial difficulties contributed much to the shaping of the town. The Clifton family of Lytham bought the Blackpool lands and sold them again in 1860 in small lots. Much of the town fell by this means into the hands of small speculative builders and was covered with close-packed terraced houses. When

PLATE 36

An aerial view of Southport: in the foreground is the promenade built on the site of a line of sand-dunes. The tree-lined boulevards of late Victorian Southport stretch away into the middle distance. In the background are the neat copses and dark ploughed soils on the site of Martin Mere.

Porter wrote his *History of the Fylde* in 1876 the resort was growing rapidly. He mentions the "terraces and villas that were being built opposite the sea and near the Lytham Road." "Building is at present being pushed forward with great activity, houses springing up in endless succession along the sides of thoroughfares but recently mapped." After 1890, when it laid itself out to cater for the working classes of the industrial towns, it grew at an enormous speed. And its dreary streets of boarding houses might easily belong to Burnley or Bolton. Much of the town seems strangely out of place under the rain-washed skies and the searchingly bright sunshine which this coast so often enjoys. The long terraces look crude and garish without a veil of smoke and a patina of soot.

IV

Roads, Canals, and Railways

In 1725 Lancashire's first Turnpike Act allowed the merchants of Liverpool to make a road to the edge of the coalfield at Prescot. Before this time Lancashire seems to have had fewer main roads than much of the rest of England. Ogilby's *Britannia* (1675) shows the great road to the north, passing through Warrington, Preston, and Lancaster, as the main route through the county. Apart from this road, first established by the Romans, Manchester was an important centre of communications in the pre-turnpike age.

A network of lanes and pack-horse tracks covered the rest of the county, connecting farms with villages and villages with market centres. Many old lanes and footpaths are probably related to the creation of the large parishes in this bleak and thinly populated part of England before the Norman Conquest, and many more originated in the great colonization movement of the twelfth and thirteenth centuries (Fig. 4). Thus the huge medieval parish of Whalley stretched southwards from the Ribble to include the moorlands of Rossendale Forest, and several of the early roads through Rossendale point towards the parish church at Whalley. Eighteenth-century maps, like those of Moll (1753) and Bowen (1767), show a road leading from Haslingden across the bare moors by Huncoat and Altham to Whalley village. Parts of this track have since disappeared completely, and on the hillsides above the smoking industrial town of Accrington the old road is scarcely distinguishable among a tangle of farm lanes.

Several of these roads across the hill-tops of Rossendale were abandoned after the building of the turnpikes through the valleys in the years round about 1800. Previously they had been busy with the caravans of ponies that carried cloth to the markets in Rochdale and Manchester. The Limersgate, a moorland track from Rochdale to Clitheroe, tells of a trade that disappeared when the Industrial Revolution produced a drastic change in communications. Trains of ponies carried lime along this road from the kilns at Clitheroe. With the opening of the Rochdale Canal in 1804 this traffic disappeared as the growing towns of the Manchester Plain began to buy their lime for building from North Derbyshire.

Before 1800 the ferries and low-tide roads across the mud-flats of the Mersey, the Ribble, and Morecambe Bay were of considerable importance. The most spectacular of these treacherous routes connected Hest Bank and Kents Bank, a distance of seven miles across the north-eastern recess of Morecambe Bay. From Cartmel a shorter passage across the Leven Sands took the guided convoys of waggons into the remote Furness peninsula. Today there is little to remind one of this main road into Furness. The branches of trees that acted as beacons at the crossings of the main tidal channels have long been washed away by the sea.

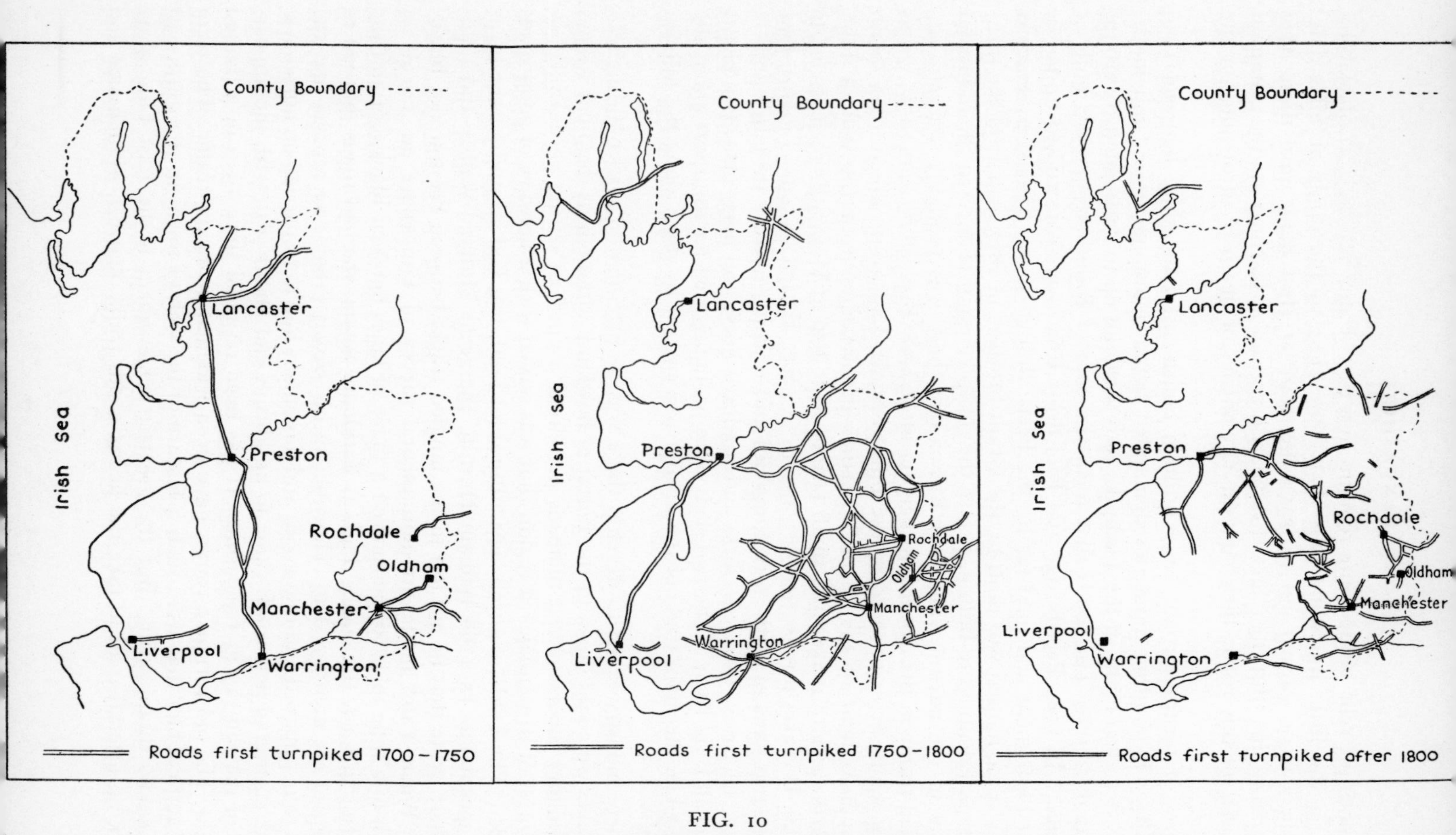

FIG. 10

Turnpike Roads in Lancashire, 1700-1840.

A picturesque relic of the route remains in a row of nine yew trees at Slackwood farm on the little limestone hills that come close to the sands at Silverdale. Travellers were warned not to leave the shore at Hest Bank until these trees appeared in line. But the pages of the parish register at Cartmel are the grimmest memorial to this road; they contain 145 entries of death by drowning on the sands.

Scores of turnpike roads were built in South-east Lancashire between 1750 and 1840. Expanding industries demanded better communications, and in the years after 1800 many of the Turnpike Acts were put up to Parliament by groups of manufacturers. The roads that form the core of Ramsbottom were built as turnpikes. In 1789 Peel Bridge and Peel Brow Road were constructed under an Act of Parliament and paid for by the Peels. Bolton Street, flanked by terraces of grey stone houses, was built by the Grant brothers in 1815 as part of the turnpike from Edenfield to Bolton. Before the turnpike roads connected the industrial villages in the narrow valleys of Rossendale there was probably scarcely any wheeled traffic in the district. Robertson in *Rochdale Past and Present* (1875) writes that waggons first appeared in the hills of South Lancashire about 1775 "with the improvement of the roads." Further proof comes from the will of John Haworth, a cloth-maker and small farmer who died at Horncliffe in Rossendale in 1766. It makes no mention of waggons or carts. He left "a pair of looms, four wheels, two pairs of cards, a twining mill and warping irons, i' th' lofts" and "a plough, a harrow, two sleds, forks and spades, a horse and horse gear, two beasts and a calf i' th' barn." The two sleds were probably used for transport about the farm, while the main trade of the district was carried by pony along the hill-top tracks.

Where industry failed to develop there was no incentive to road building. No turnpikes were laid down in the Forest of Bowland, although its deep-cut valleys and billowy moor-covered plateaus presented a physical setting very similar to the Forest of Rossendale—a region that was served with a network of good roads by 1820. The Fylde, a purely agricultural lowland, was bad ground for the turnpike speculator. In 1788 William Hutton, the great Midland walker and topographer, wrote that he got lost in the tangled tracks between Preston and Blackpool. When Yates made his monumental survey of Lancashire on a scale of 1 inch to a mile in 1786, he showed a maze of lanes between Blackpool and the old Roman road, the Danes' Pad, at Kirkham. Again, the bad roads that led to Blackpool are mentioned by Thornber in his *History* (1837); he reports that the lanes were unpaved and that goods and passengers had to be carried on horseback.

The cutting of new roads came to an abrupt end about 1840 with the appearance of the railway in Lancashire. It has been resumed since 1920 in a limited fashion. The old turnpike routes have been widened for heavy traffic. The tram lines and cobbles that were such a feature of the web of towns in the south-east are rapidly disappearing. But the greatest achievement is the East Lancashire Road, an arterial road to take the heavy goods traffic between Manchester and

Liverpool (Plate 37). It by-passes large towns like St. Helens, and with its cuttings and embankments borrows from the techniques of the railway engineer.

Bridges

The earliest documentary record of a bridge in Lancashire dates back to the beginning of the thirteenth century. Many more appear in the following century. The bridges across the Mersey and Sankey Brook at Warrington are mentioned in 1305. There was a bridge over the Ribble at Preston in 1302 and another

PLATE 37

The East Lancashire Road: the arterial road that was cut between Liverpool and Manchester in the 1930's.

across the Lune at Lancaster in 1324. They all lie on the ancient road to the north, the main route through Lancashire.

These dates provide no hint of the time when a bridge was first built at these places. Watkin, who made the first systematic study of Roman remains in Lancashire, believed there was a bridge across the Lune by the second century A.D. There was certainly a wooden bridge at Lancaster in King John's reign. In 1216 the Abbot of Furness was made responsible for its repair, and he was allowed to draw timber for it from the royal forest near the town. When Leland journeyed through Lancashire he found good stone bridges across all the main rivers on the road to the north. At Preston he rode over "the great stone bridge of Ribble having five great arches," and "by the town's end of Garstang I rode over a great stone bridge on Wyre." The increased traffic of carts and waggons on the new turnpike roads towards the end of the eighteenth century caused the re-building of most of these bridges. A new bridge was opened at Lancaster in 1788. It stands a quarter of a mile up the Lune from the old bridge that lay immediately under the slope of the round hill crowned by the parish church. The adjustments to the street plan of Lancaster brought about by the building of this new bridge

PLATE 38

Old Hodder Bridge: a pack-horse bridge built by public subscription in 1563.

are clearly apparent today. The old centre of the town, clustered about the castle and St. Mary's, now seems strangely isolated from the north bank of the river.

Many Lancashire bridges date from the eighteenth century. This period of bridge-building was started by an Act of Parliament in 1670 in which complaint was made of Lancashire's "great and deep rivers, which run across and through the common and public highways and roads, which many times cannot be passed over without hazard and loss of the lives and goods of the inhabitants and travellers for want of convenient, good and sufficient bridges." In the seventeenth century indeed there was only one bridge across the Ribble above Preston.

An attractive pair of bridges spans the Hodder where it cuts through a shallow, wooded gorge, a mile above its junction with the Ribble. One, a graceful, high-backed pack-horse bridge, was built in 1563 (Plate 38). This reddish-grey sandstone bridge seems to have been built by public subscription, for there is a record of Richard Nowell who gave ten shillings "to the Collectors towards the building of Hodder Bridge." A note also exists of the sum of £70, paid to the mason, Roger Crossley, for building this bridge. A few yards above the narrow, grass-grown pack-horse bridge the modern road from Stoneyhurst to Mitton crosses the Hodder on a bridge of three arches, built in 1826. It was erected when Macadam reconstructed the road from Longridge to Clitheroe, and here made one of his first experiments with a new road surface.

Canals

The great wave of canal building that ushered in the Industrial Revolution started in South Lancashire, and was largely financed by the merchant classes. The capital for the Sankey Navigation (1755) was raised by the merchants of Liverpool, and a group of Lancaster's West Indian traders and bankers applied in 1792 for an Act of Parliament to build a canal from Westmorland to the Wigan coalfield (Plate 39). This had the aim of carrying coal into the farmlands of the Fylde, and of exporting lime from the bare grey hills about Carnforth to improve the acid soils in the south of the county.

The Sankey Navigation follows the valley of the Sankey Brook into the heart of the St. Helens coalfield. Although it is scarcely 200 years since John Ashton, a Liverpool cheesemonger and member of the Company of African Merchants, invested £9,000 in the Sankey Canal, the story of its construction has already become an object of historical research. The canal was surveyed and engineered by Henry Berry, Liverpool's second dock engineer. Berry was born close to St. Helens, and as a boy he probably knew well the streams that flow from the Billinge Ridge into the Sankey Brook. He lies buried in the yard of the dissenters' chapel that is now the Ormskirk Road Congregational Church, at the very centre of St. Helens.

Berry's intimate knowledge of the countryside through which he built the Sankey Navigation contributed much to the success of this daring and expensive piece of engineering. Perhaps his experience of the bad winter floods in the shallow streams about St. Helens led him to abandon the original project to deepen the bed of the Sankey Brook and to substitute a scheme for a canal. His obituary notice in the *Liverpool Mercury* of 7 August, 1812, tells us that he discovered "after an attentive survey" that it was impossible to make the Sankey Brook navigable and he put up another scheme for a dead-water canal. The work "was commenced on the 5th September, 1755, and concealed from all but one proprietor."

It is strange to think that the third great piece of engineering in Lancashire, after the construction of Steers' two docks at Liverpool, was accomplished in an atmosphere of secrecy. The first mention of the canal in contemporary newspapers and journals appears in an advertisement in the *Liverpool Chronicle* of 1757 which reports that "the Sankey Brook Navigation is now open for the passage of flats to the Haydock and Parr collieries." Research has revealed no eye-witness account of the fantastic scenes in the meadows of the Sankey Brook during the cutting of the canal, though the Liverpool papers, *Whitworth's Manchester Magazine* and *Eyre's Weekly Journal*, published in Warrington, might well have carried reports

PLATE 39

Lancaster Canal: an eighteenth-century bridge across the canal that was built by the merchants of Lancaster to carry coal from the Wigan coalfield to the north of the county.

of the hundreds of navvies, masons, and carpenters who were transforming this fragment of the Lancashire landscape with only the most primitive tools.

When the Sankey Navigation was finished it started an even more complicated process of economic change in the dull countryside on the north shore of the Mersey. The output of coal rose enormously. In 1758 Sarah Clayton, owner of the manor of Parr and a woman of great business ability, advertised her coal pits at Parr in the *Liverpool Chronicle*: "two delfs are already open and a quantity of each delf got ready for sale." By 1771 a Parliamentary report said that 45,568 tons of coal had been carried down the canal to Liverpool and another 44,152 tons had gone in the same year to Warrington and Northwich. From Liverpool some of the coal was carried across the Atlantic to the North American colonies, where New York was a big importer.

Adventurers like Peter Orrett began to build wharves and warehouses on the canal. He gave up a steady job as surveyor to the Prescot to Warrington turnpike, but went bankrupt in an attempt to create a centre of trade at Bewsey Lock. In 1773 the British Cast Plate Glass Company built a factory at Ravenhead, not far from the end of the canal. Hughes, Williams, and Company established a copper-smelting works on its banks in 1780. The raw material was carried from the rich mines at the Parys Mountain in Anglesey along the Mersey and the Sankey Canal to the cheap coal at the Ravenhead smelters. Later, in 1828, the chemical works of Muspratt and Gamble were established within sight of this murky ribbon of water, and towards the close of the century the huge glass factories of Pilkingtons spread around the terminal basins of the canal.

The Sankey Navigation started a train of industries that gave rise to a new town—St. Helens. It also gave fabulous profits to its small number of investors. In 1814, Michael Hughes, manager of the Ravenhead copper works and squire of Sutton Hall, offered a part of one of his shares in the Sankey Navigation to Thomas Case at the rate of £1,300 per share. The Sankey Canal Company united with the St. Helens and Runcorn Gap Railway in 1845; later they were both swallowed by the London and North-western Railway. Before the first World War there was little traffic on the canal, and it became completely derelict in 1919, when only seven "flats" were booked through Newton Common Lock on the way to St. Helens.

While the Sankey Navigation was planned in an atmosphere of secrecy, and its engineering later attributed to James Brindley, the canal which the Duke of Bridgewater financed from Worsley to Manchester soon became one of the wonders of England. Arthur Young devotes the whole of the nineteenth letter of his *Six Months' Tour* to a minutely detailed account of its embankments, bridges, wharves, and weirs. The most impressive sight for this eighteenth-century tourist was the mile-long tunnel at Worsley, "which is a subterraneous canal hewn out of the rock to a great length and extending into the heart of the coal mines." Even today, when our imagination can be held suspended by the sweeping façade of the Mersey tunnel or the intricate iron skeleton of Widnes transporter bridge, James Brindley's canal tunnel is an impressive sight. Its mouth lies low at the foot of a red sandstone cliff that bears the chisel marks of the quarrymen who cut much of the stone for the bridges and locks from this place. Now it looks as abandoned as any of the waterways of Lancashire (Plate 40). The canal, a still ribbon of brilliant orange chrome, emerges from the darkness of the tunnel into a dense marsh of tall reeds. The steep slopes flanking the cliff are overgrown with a thin green wood that has sown itself over the naked spoil heaps since the busy years about 1800 when trains of barges carried out their cargoes of coal for Manchester.

The canal fever reached its height in the 1790's. Parliament passed an Act for the Manchester and Bolton Canal in 1791. In the following year a canal was projected from Manchester to Ashton and Oldham. The idea of the Rochdale Canal appeared in 1794. This ambitious plan connected Lancashire with Yorkshire through the Littleborough Gap. A chain of large reservoirs was constructed on the moors above Rochdale to feed the canal with water, largely because the mill owners believed that water drawn direct from the brooks would interfere with their power supplies. One of these reservoirs—Hollingworth Lake—became

PLATE 40

The entrance to the Duke of Bridgewater's coal mines at Worsley. The red sandstone cliff above the tunnel was used as a quarry to supply building-stone for James Brindley's canal engineering between Worsley and Manchester.

a pleasure resort for the people of the cotton towns after 1850. A paddle steamer used to thrash between the two hotels on its shores, and the railway brought crowds of day-trippers and Sunday-school outings from miles around. But today, Hollingworth Lake is scarcely less derelict than the canal that coils round the hillsides below.

Lancashire contains no more striking memorial to the first stage of the Industrial Revolution than its silent canals with their towpaths crumbling into the still waters amid the ragged patches of grey-green reeds. They were the work of engineers of the eminence of John Rennie, who constructed the Ulverston Sea Canal (Plate 41) and the Lancaster Canal, of engineers whose skill is commemorated in the embankments and cuttings which the passing of time has fitted so harmoniously into the landscape. In places the modest engineering of the canal flowers into something more magnificent. At Lancaster, Rennie carried his canal across the Lune on a high graceful aqueduct of local stone that immediately became one of the sights of the town. John Britton, in his *Beauties of England and Wales* (1808), writes of the Lune aqueduct: "It is justly considered the most magnificent structure of its kind that has ever been erected in Great Britain, and may fairly vie with any of the pompous works of the Romans. . . . The foundation

PLATE 41

The Ulverston Sea Canal built by John Rennie in 1795 in an effort to maintain Ulverston's position as a port.

alone is said to have cost £15,000, and the superstructure above double that sum, although the stone was obtained within about one mile and a half of the place. . . . The whole bridge has a handsome cornice and every part of it is designed with strict regard to strength, durability and elegance."

Lancashire's last and greatest canal, the Manchester Ship Canal, was built between 1888 and 1894. The county's first artificial waterway, the Sankey Navigation, had been cut in secrecy, but this thirty-five-mile-long highway for ocean-going ships was born in a great blaze of publicity. Papers like *Tit-Bits*, by-products of the Education Acts of the 1870's, printed cartoons of the "Port of Manchester in 1950." In this peep into the future a pier and bathing machines compete for space with the ships that crowd together in the Trafford Park docks;

derelict Liverpool is adorned with "to let" signs. *Punch*, appealing to a more educated reader, indulged in such fantasies as "Manchester-sur-Mer. A sea-ductive prospect." In the Liverpool pantomimes of the 1880's the Ship Canal scheme was a constant object of fun and derision.

The Ship Canal provides a fitting monument to the close of the nineteenth century in Lancashire. In a period of high prosperity and with all the technological resources of the Industrial Revolution to hand, the county's great inland city was transformed into a world port. To achieve this aim, rivers were diverted,

PLATE 42

Ulverston: The Canal Head Stores, with the rough-cast treatment that is characteristic of Furness.

miles of deep cuttings were hewn and blasted through the red sandstones of the Mersey valley, and railways were carried across the new waterway on viaducts at 80 feet above the mean water level in the canal. An army of 17,000 navvies, aided by hundreds of steam engines, cranes, and dredgers, completed the task in six years. It cost over £15,000,000 and left a curious landmark on the Cheshire bank of the Mersey in Mount Manisty—a huge artificial hill of waste extracted from the cuttings about Eastham that was first used as a source of ballast and has now become a nature reserve.

Travellers in Lancashire at the close of the eighteenth century believed that the canal building of the previous fifty years had brought the county's transport system to perfection. Aikin's magnificent topographical work published in 1795—*A Description of the Country from Thirty to Forty Miles round Manchester*—was written at a time when the canal system was almost complete and when the railways were unforeseen. His title-page carries a picture of a canal aqueduct stretching across an arm of the sea, "a kind of visionary anticipation of the future wonders of canal navigation." Aikin was optimistic about the economic effect of canals: "The future progress of the county is beyond the reach of calculation. Nothing but highly flourishing manufactures can repay the expense of these designs."

PLATE 43

Chat Moss about 1830: the building of George Stephenson's railway across Chat Moss was the first great achievement of the railway engineers of the nineteenth century. The rectangular network of ditches shows this wilderness in the process of reclamation.

But the huge lobe of bare hills and deep valleys that makes up Rossendale Forest defeated the canal speculator. A scheme was suggested for a canal to connect Bury with the Leeds and Liverpool Canal through Haslingden. Baines mentions this project in his *Directory* (1825) and adds a critical comment that a railway would be a more suitable proposition.

Railways

The Liverpool and Manchester Railway, constructed between 1826 and 1830, was an experiment in public transport that aroused a vast amount of controversy. A journey from Manchester Exchange to Liverpool Lime Street can still revive some of the impact which this railway made on its contemporaries, especially if one takes one of the topographical railway guides that were published in the 1830's.

A few miles out from the suburbs of Manchester, George Stephenson's railway crosses Chat Moss (Plate 43). The floating of the line across this peat morass on bundles of heather and wooden hurdles was one of the first great feats of railway engineering. The reclamation of this wilderness had started in 1805. Today the dark soils are closely farmed in small-holdings, but in 1838, when Freeling wrote his *Companion to the Liverpool and Manchester Railway*, he noted that "half a mile

PLATE 44

The railway viaduct over the Sankey Canal: an historic place in the Lancashire landscape where the county's first railway crosses the first canal.

from Bury Lane station we enter the dreary waste of Chat Moss. Some attempts at cultivation will be perceived—successful or not in point of profit, time will tell."

Between Newton and St. Helens Junction are several places of great historic interest. At Parkside, a few yards to the east of Newton station, the Liverpool M.P., Huskisson, was killed by a train in the elaborate opening ceremonies of the railway. At Earlstown a small industrial settlement grew around the railway-waggon works. Its drab streets of red brick could easily belong to Wolverton, Crewe, or Swindon. Beyond Earlstown the line crosses the Sankey Navigation on a high viaduct, perhaps the most historic point in Lancashire's system of communications, at the intersection of the county's first canal and its first railway.

George Stephenson's railway enters Liverpool through a succession of deep cuttings in the New Red Sandstone. The Olive Mount Cutting at Edge Hill is over two miles long and in places more than 80 feet deep (Plate 45). These narrow ravines, their vertical faces glowing red in the afternoon sunshine, are still an impressive feature of the landscape. They are even more astonishing when we recall that they are part of one of the world's earliest railways. The Victorian compiler of Murray's *Handbook for Lancashire* (1880) reminds us that "480,000 cubic yards of sandstone were removed from the Olive Mount Cutting." We may be less impressed by such statistics in these days, but it is a pity that the elaborate

PLATE 45

Olive Mount Cutting: a dramatic feature of the Liverpool and Manchester Railway under construction. The cutting is over two miles long and in places more than eighty feet deep.

memorial arch at Edge Hill has not survived. When we are constantly reminded of the bankruptcy of our national railway system, it is worth while remembering that the pioneers of the Liverpool and Manchester Railway could erect a memorial to their efforts before they had seen a dividend.

After 1840 South Lancashire was rapidly covered with a network of railways that eventually coalesced into the Lancashire and Yorkshire and London and North-western Companies. North Lancashire, always a remote and isolated region, had a separate railway history until the Furness lines were swallowed up by the L.M.S. in the amalgamation of 1923. The Furness Railway was designed to carry iron ore from the mines in the Dalton district to the jetties at Barrow and Rampside. The first strip of line from Barrow to Dalton was opened in 1846, but the most important event in the railway history of Furness was the completion of the line from Ulverston to Carnforth in 1857. Its two great embankments and iron viaducts, stretched across the tidal sands of the Leven and Kent, effectively broke the isolation of the peninsula.

The Furness Railway system radically changed the geography of North Lancashire. Cartmel ceased to be a busy junction on the coach and waggon road

PLATE 46

Roa Island railway station: an Edwardian Sunday afternoon. In the distance is the embankment that connects Roa Island with the mainland, built by John Abel Smith in the 1840's as part of a grandiose scheme for a railway from London to Glasgow with a ferry across the mouth of Morecambe Bay from Fleetwood.

across the sands. Ulverston lost its place as the regional capital of Furness, and, among the fields on the edge of Walney Channel, Barrow arose as a port and steel town, shaped and governed by the directors of the railway company. When the ambitions of James Ramsden burned at their brightest he hoped that Barrow might become another Liverpool, a great port with a line of docks stretching from Barrow Old Island to Roa Island at the south entrance to the Walney

Channel. The disillusionment of these hopes can be sensed today in the derelict terminus of the Furness Railway on Roa Island (Plate 46).

As you walk through the abandoned station or stroll along the embankment that joins Roa Island to the mainland at Rampside, it is difficult to believe that this was an important terminus in the 1870's where trains unloaded their passengers on to the steamers for the Isle of Man and Ireland. Now it is hard to find someone there who will row you across the half-mile of Piel Channel to the battered ruin of the fourteenth-century castle on Piel Island.

The plan to develop Roa Island is one of the many attractive failures that litter our railway history. John Abel Smith, a rich London banker, bought this tiny rock, close to the deep water of Piel Channel, in 1840. Two years previously Decimus Burton had marked out the streets of the new town and port of Fleetwood on the opposite shore of Morecambe Bay. Smith hoped that Roa Island would become part of a route from London to Glasgow, the journey being made by train to Fleetwood, thence by ferry across the mouth of Morecambe Bay, and on to Scotland by a railway to be constructed along the Cumberland coast. Smith built the causeway "to connect Roa Island with the neighbouring island of Great Britain," as he picturesquely expressed his enterprise. He completed Piel Pier in 1847 and in the following year the "Helvellyn" was running a daily service to Fleetwood. The Furness Railway Company bought Roa Island in 1852 after a storm had badly damaged Smith's property and his romantic idea of a main line to Glasgow had been shattered by the building of the present railway over Shap Fell.

Until 1882 Piel Pier was the main terminus for passenger ships leaving Barrow; after that date all the traffic was removed to the Ramsden Dock Station. In 1891 the Pier was demolished, so that today there is little to recall this Victorian enterprise apart from a short street of cottages, brought into existence by the railway.

V

The Landscape Today

As one travels through Lancashire today, on every hand there are objects in the landscape that recall persons and periods from the county's history. From the dull coastline at the Mersey mouth to the rolling plateaus of Rossendale and Bowland the scenery has been fashioned in every detail to serve the purposes of men. Today the major tasks of transformation seem to be complete. It took a thousand years to clear the natural woodlands; the great mosses disappeared within a century; in less than a hundred years the coalfields were covered with a morass of houses, mines, and mills. It is hard to imagine that any fundamental changes of this magnitude lie ahead, now that the pioneering stages of agriculture

PLATE 47

The Duddon valley: the frontier of the improved land in High Furness. The walls are composed of thin slate slabs and irregular boulders gathered in the making of the fields.

and industry are over. In the future the landscape of Lancashire will be largely trimmed to the deep and uncontrollable currents of economics and to the changes in industrial technique. But it is doubtful whether Lancashire will ever again experience the vitality of the Victorian Age.

The Victorians neglected the countryside of Lancashire. Towards the close of the nineteenth century, as cheap grain and frozen meat flowed into the industrial towns in exchange for the miles of cotton cloth that rolled off the looms, many of the high hill farms were abandoned, while the bleached pastures in the neighbourhood of the big towns concentrated on the production of fresh milk. Two world wars and the emergence of a fresh pattern of world trade in the middle of the twentieth century have had their effect upon the scenery of Lancashire. The most notable is the attempt to make better use of the high, abandoned hill pastures. In Rossendale the bright green carpets of sown grasses are beginning to invade the monotonous yellow-brown mat of derelict "nardus" pasture. But even though we have learnt a lot about the chemistry of soils, we have forgotten some of the valuable crafts of the early nineteenth-century farmers. The art of building dry-stone walls is dead in Lancashire, and today the universal fencing materials are barbed wire and concrete posts. On the Lancashire Plain arable farming has made a significant return in a region that was predominantly pastoral in the late 1930's. The small hedged enclosures, an object of complaint by Aikin and Holt at the close of the eighteenth century, are beginning to disappear. The widespread use of the tractor is encouraging the creation of larger fields.

But all of these are minor changes in the established landscape. Nowhere can one point to the kinds of major change that have occurred in the past when the "statesmen" hacked their farms out of the wilderness of High Furness in the sixteenth century. Nothing today compares with the changes that followed the enclosure of the high wastes at the turn of the eighteenth century. W. S. Garnett in his prize-winning essay, *Farming in Lancashire* (1849), describes the improvement of Ellel Moor on the western edge of Bowland Forest. Mr. Hinde described to Garnett the creation of a new field from the moor in the 1840's: "I removed nine hundred and twenty one-horse cart loads of stones from the land after it was drained and trenched, which I sold to the Surveyor of Roads, and which paid for the removal, the road being alongside the field, besides seventy loads of good rubble walling-stones from the large stones we had to break up with hammers and wedges." No such scene would greet the traveller in Lancashire today!

No new land is being broken for farming in Lancashire and the towns have stopped their rapid expansion. The sharp decline of population that appeared in the textile towns after 1930 was only arrested by the second world war and the boom years of full employment since 1945. But already a brief and sudden trade recession in 1952 has shown that Oldham, Bolton, and Rochdale might be thrown back to the difficulties of the great slump. In an effort to save the "old" industrial areas of the British Isles, the State has intervened to dictate the sites of new industries. The drift to the south has been arrested by government decree and expanding new industries are now encouraged to settle in the derelict valleys of South Wales, on the coalfield of Northumberland and Durham, and in the depressed area of Merseyside.

If John Whittaker, described by Butterworth as "the cotton prince of Mossley," could return to the industrial village he created at Hurst, he would perhaps better express the slow change that has come over industrial Lancashire than we who live in the midst of the process. Whittaker built a small cotton mill at Higher Hurst near Ashton-under-Lyne in 1808. By 1840 he employed 1,000 hands and, in the words of Butterworth, "he had been the means in a few years of converting a mere group of houses into a large and increasing village." . . . "He produced upwards of forty thousand pounds of yarn weekly, and eight thousand pieces of power loom cloth weekly." Today Hurst consists of a few parallel streets of dreary terraces, shadowed by the huge cube of Whittaker's mill. Above its six storeys rises a tall square water tower with the name Whittakers Limited imprinted in glistening white brick. This huge mill has broken all contact with the cotton industry. It became derelict in the great slump, when its machinery was dismantled and sold to the scrap metal merchants. In the second World War it was an army depôt. Now this palatial experiment in factory architecture of a

PLATE 48

The derelict Oldham and Ashton Canal.

century ago is divided among a number of light industries. In the main spinning mill that housed the biggest beam engine in the north of England they work day and night putting beer into bottles. Another part of John Whittaker's building makes leather handbags; the boiler house supplies power to a furniture factory. The earliest part of the building erected by John Whittaker stands empty and quiet. Its windows have long been smashed, the walls are starting to crumble, and rain streams through the broken roof, dripping from floor to floor and coursing along the arcades of decaying cast-iron pillars.

This nineteenth-century industrial village has lost its primary industries of cotton spinning and weaving, and in 1929, at the time of the economic collapse, it gave up its political individuality, when the urban district council abandoned its power to Ashton Corporation. The sea of "modern semis," sweeping up from Ashton, has swamped Hurst on all sides—uniformly ugly in their coat of glazed, sootless, dull red brick.

The industrial structure of Lancashire is undergoing radical change, and at the same time the twentieth century has abandoned the Victorian attitude to towns. The nineteenth-century towns sprawled vigorously over the coal-rich

PLATE 49

A mid-Victorian Methodist chapel at Lumb-in-Rossendale.

plains. Today we only seem concerned about solving the problems left by Victorian industrialism. The County Planning Office calculates that more than half a million people in the slums of the overgrown cities need to be rehoused. The application of the principles of large-scale planning has suggested the creation of new towns to solve this problem. Three new towns were proposed, at Garstang, Parbold, and Leyland. It was planned to develop Parbold into a town of 45,000, housing the "overspill" population of Liverpool. The quiet village of Garstang was to be inflated to 50,000 with a population drawn from Manchester. Already some dark ministerial decision has caused the abandonment of the scheme for

Garstang, and the new town at Parbold has been transferred to the straggly mining village of Skelmersdale.

Until now the thoughts and ideas of the town-planner have had very little influence on the landscape of Lancashire. There has been a modest amount of building at Leyland since the war. In contrast to the last century this seems to be an age that plans superbly but accomplishes little. The Victorians created a steel town on a salt marsh, turned Manchester into a port with the cutting of the Ship Canal, and erected countless churches, chapels, town halls, and mills. Today

PLATE 50

The historic Lancashire scene at Failsworth: here a Roman road is cut by the abandoned Oldham and Ashton Canal. In the distance are the mill-chimneys of Oldham.

we can count the cost of three new towns in Lancashire and the expansion of eight villages at £330,000,000, but we cannot find the capital. The Victorians with their sixty-six-hour week, the plain living of the counting house and the deep puritanism of the chapel, and a trade that was expanding into every corner of the globe, accumulated the liquid capital to invest in the scores of new towns. The economic climate has changed deeply. The means of expansion are no longer there and the Lancashire landscape stands complete, largely a gift of the Victorian Age.

Select Bibliography

Aikin, J., *Description of the Country from Thirty to Forty Miles round Manchester*, 1795.
Allison, J. E., *The Mersey Estuary*, 1949.
Armstrong, R. G., "The Rise of Morecambe, 1820-1862," *T.H.S.*, C, 1948.
Atkinson, J. C., and Brownbill, J., *The Coucher Book of Furness Abbey*, six vols., Chetham Society, 1886-1919.
Bagley, J. J., "The Foundation and Financing of Upholland Grammar School," *T.H.S.*, C, 1948.
Bailey, F. A., "Early Coal-mining in Prescot," *T.H.S.*, LXXXXIX, 1947.
Baines, E., *History of Lancashire*, 1836 (revised edn. 1888).
Baines, E., *History, Directory, and Gazetteer of the County of Lancaster*, two vols., 1825.
Barker, T. C., "The Sankey Navigation," *T.H.S.*, C, 1948.
Barker, T. C., and Newbury, N. F., *The Growth of St. Helens*, 1950.
Barnes, F., *Barrow and District*, 1951.
Barton, B. T., *History of Bury*, 1874.
Bateson, H., *A History of Oldham*, 1949.
Beamont, W., *Walks about Warrington*, 1887.
Bland, E., *Annals of Southport and District*, 1887.
Brockbank, J., *A History of St. Helens*, 1896.
Butterworth, E., *Statistical Sketch of the County Palatine of Lancashire*, 1833.
Butterworth, E., *Historical Sketches of Oldham*, 1849.
Butterworth, J., *The History of Oldham*, 1817.
Carter, G. A., *Warrington Hundred*, 1949.
Cowper, H. S., *Hawkshead: its History, Antiquities, and Folklore*, 1899.
Doe, B., "Notes on Decimus Burton," Fleetwood Public Library MSS., 1951.
Ekwall, E., *The Place-Names of Lancashire*, 1922.
Elliot, W. Hume, *The County of the Cheeryble Brothers*, 1893.
Fell, A., *The Early Iron Industry of Furness and District*, 1908.
Freeling's London, Birmingham, Liverpool, and Manchester Railway Companion, 1838.
Garnett, W. S., "Farming of Lancashire," *Journal of the Royal Agricultural Society*, 1849.
Gore, G. Perry, *The Story of the Ancient Parochial Chapelry of St. Mary's, Oldham*, 1906.
Harris, J. R., "Michael Hughes of Sutton," *T.H.S.*, C, 1948.
Harrison, W., "The Development of the Turnpike System in Lancashire and Cheshire," *Transactions of the Lancashire and Cheshire Antiquarian Society*, IV, 1886.
Harrison, W., "Ancient Fords, Ferries and Bridges in Lancashire," *Transactions of the Lancashire and Cheshire Antiquarian Society*, XII-XIII, 1895-6.
Hesketh, R. F., *Sir Peter Hesketh-Fleetwood, Founder of the Town and Port of Fleetwood*, 1951.
Hewitson, A., *History of Preston*, 1883.
Historical Account of the Port of Fleetwood (Lancashire and Yorkshire Railway, 1877).
Holt, J., *A General View of the Agriculture of the County of Lancaster*, 1795.
Hutton, W., *A Description of Blackpool*, 1789.
Langshaw, A., "The Hundred Bridges of the Hundred of Blackburn in the Seventeenth Century," *T.H.S.*, LXXXXVIII, 1946.
Leach, F., *Barrow-in-Furness: Its Rise and Progress with Brief Sketches of its Leading Industries*, 1872.
Lucas, J., *History of Warton*, written 1710-44 and edited by J. R. Ford and J. A. F. Maitland, 1931.
Manley, G., "The Climate of Lancashire," *Memoirs and Proceedings of the Manchester Literary and Philosophical Society*, 1946-7.
Middleton, J., *Oldham Past and Present*, 1903.
Newbigging, T., *History of the Forest of Rossendale*, 1868.
North Lonsdale Magazine and Furness Miscellany, 1894-1900.
Park, J., *Some Ulverston Records*, 1932.
Parkinson, C. N., *The Rise of the Port of Liverpool*, 1952.
Pollard, J., *Handbook and Guide to Preston*, 1882.
Porter, J., *History of the Fylde*, 1876.
Pyne, W. H., *Lancashire Illustrated*, 1831.
Rance, C. E. de, *The Superficial Geology of the Country adjoining the Coasts of South-west Lancashire*, 1877.
Richardson, J., *Furness Past and Present*, 1880.
Richardson, J., *Barrow-in-Furness: Its History, Development, Commerce, Industries, and Institutions*, 1881.
Robertson, W., *Rochdale Past and Present*, 1875; *Old and New Rochdale*, 1878.
Schofield, M. M., *Outlines of an Economic History of Lancaster*, two vols., 1946.
Shaw, G., *Oldham: Local Notes and Gleanings*, 1887-8.
Shaw, J. B., *History of the Port of Lancaster*, 1926.
Shaw, R. Cunliffe, *Kirkham in Amounderness*, 1950.
Smith, W., *Lancashire: Report of the Land Utilization Survey*, Part XLV, 1941.
Tait, J., *The Medieval English Borough*, 1936; *Medieval Manchester and the Beginnings of Lancashire*, 1904.
Tait, A., *History of the Oldham Lyceum, 1839-1897*, 1897.
Taylor, W. Cooke, *Notes of a Tour in the Manufacturing Districts of Lancashire*, 1842.
The Victoria County History of Lancashire, ed. W. Farrer and J. Brownbill, 1906-14, eight vols.
Thornber, W., *An Historical Account of Blackpool*, 1837.
Tupling, G. H., *The Economic History of Rossendale*, 1927.
Wainwright, F. T., "The Anglian Settlement of Lancashire," *T.H.S.*, LXXXXIII, 1941.
Wainwright, F. T., "North-west Mercia," *T.H.S.*, LXXXXIV, 1942.
Wainwright, F. T., "Field Names of the Amounderness Hundred," *T.H.S.*, LXXXXVII, 1945.
Walker, F., *The Historical Geography of South-west Lancashire*, 1937.
Watkin, W. T., *Roman Lancashire*, 1883.
West, T., *Antiquities of Furness*, 1774.
Whitaker, T. D., *The History of Manchester*, four vols., 1771.
Whittle, P., *The Borough of Preston*, 1821; *History of Southport*, 1830.
Young, Arthur, *A Six Months' Tour through the North of England*, 1771.

Note.—*T.H.S.* refers to the *Transactions of the Historic Society of Lancashire and Cheshire*.

Index

Italic figures in parentheses refer to illustrations and maps.